immune system relaxation

Stress T'ai chi pressure
the good and the bad
adrenaline treat yourself

Paula Ceccaldi
Agnès Diricq
Clémentine Bagieu

CASSELL&CO

35% of sales representatives suffer from an anxious–depressive syndrome; 8% suffer from a depressive state. ▶ 43

Caffeine can remain active in the body up to 10 hours after it is absorbed. ▶ 78

15 minutes *rest after lunch (without coffee) is enough to recharge your batteries: in an armchair, at the office or at home.* ▶ 84

15%

of the British population are users of anxiolytic, antidepressant and sleeping tablets. 94

People who undergo life-threatening experiences (such as accidents, terrorist attacks, assaults or natural disasters) can, like those who witness these events, suffer what psychiatrists call post-traumatic stress disorder.

 33

Women *are the* **biggest users** *of psychoactive* **drugs.**

▶ 94

'Stress'

It was in Britain that the word 'stress' was first used as the name of a **medical condition.** The term was used in the 17th century to 14 mean suffering, deprivation, ordeal and adversity: in short, misery.

Stress

is the end result of all the hormonal and neurochemical upheavals brought on by anything that threatens a person's physical and psychological well-being.

 14

Find a quiet place, sit comfortably, listen to your breathing for a few minutes and relax a little. ▶ 87

Why not change your appearance? Get rid of all those grey and black items from your wardrobe and give yourself a new self-image. ▶ 83

Energy exists in two forms: yin (negative) and yang (positive). ▶ 90

It is essential for individuals to find their own way to manage stress. Techniques such as t'ai chi are popular methods of escaping the monotony of routine. ▶ 87

Relaxation and peace are intimately linked with the body and with breathing, as well as with our state of health.

 ▶ 87

Why not bring back the siesta? ▶ 84

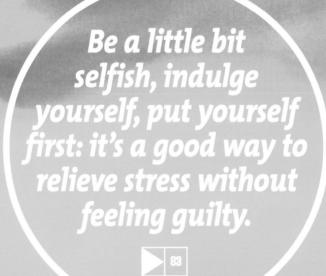

Be a little bit selfish, indulge yourself, put yourself first: it's a good way to relieve stress without feeling guilty.

▶ 83

'He advised Ronnie to think nice, soothing thoughts in bed to calm him and lull him into sleep. Nothing about sex or work or money. Pleasant, green-trees kind of stuff. Ronnie took the doctor at his word and tried the technique. For weeks it had not worked. No sylvan musings seemed to help Ronnie sleep. Then he decided to personalise the process.' *Robert McLiam Wilson* ▶ 102

Simplify your movements, develop daily reflex actions to **free yourself of stress-inducing habits.**

 87

What **emergency action against stress** can you take at home? Essential oils and simple exercises should do the trick.

 114

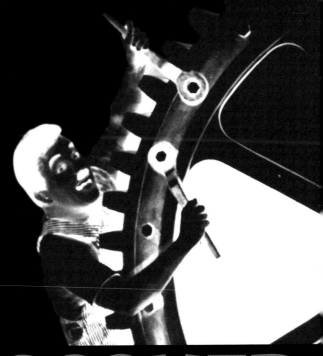

DISCOVER

STRESS IS NOT PURELY A MODERN CONCERN, BUT AN AFFLICTION THAT HAS
TROUBLED PEOPLE FOR CENTURIES. TODAY, CAUSES OF STRESS INCLUDE
WORK, MARITAL DISPUTES, MONEY WORRIES, LACK OF TIME FOR OUR
CHILDREN, AND LONELINESS. BUT STRESS CAN ONLY BE MASTERED BY
GETTING TO KNOW ITS CAUSES AND PINNING THEM DOWN.

The World Health Organization (WHO) regards stress as the 'scourge of the Western world'. According to the International Labour Organization (ILO) it has become 'one of the most serious problems of our time, not only for the individuals whose physical and mental health it endangers but also for businesses and governments'.

ARE WE MORE STRESSED THAN OUR ANCESTORS?

We tend to think that stress is a characteristic of modern life, but there is no doubt that our cave-dwelling ancestors were also under stress. However, since they spent most of their time trying to meet basic material needs, they were probably less affected than we are by the turbulence of such experiences as bereavement, love affairs, and social interaction. Constantly exposed to cold, hunger and a hostile environment swarming with predators and competing enemy tribes, their daily experience was of a never-ending fight for survival. However, prehistoric man's body, like that of all living things, was wonderfully adapted to this struggle. Faced with an attack, or with the threat of attack, his body's natural mechanisms instantly put it into a state of 'fight or flight'. The term 'stress' has come to mean a state of anguish or distress, where the body adapts to a changing environment. It provokes an innate response that is necessary for survival because it allows us to escape from dangerous situations. Our ancestors were stressed too, but thanks to progress in science and technology, the threats we face today are more psychological and emotional than physical. But the danger is no less for all that.

STRESS IS A WAY OF SURVIVING

To fight or flee from a threat is an ancient reflex action on which the survival of mankind has depended.

Although life is relatively comfortable nowadays, it is far more complex than it was centuries ago, with a proliferation of information, tasks, rules and regulations that is often hard to manage. Our environment, unlike that of our ancestors, is constantly changing – in its location (home, office, travel, town, country), in the pace of change, the level of noise, even the climate. Each new situation demands a different physiological adaptation from us. On top of all this, we feel a sense of loss of control over our environment – in other words, a loss of free will. Modern life limits our room to manoeuvre. When faced with a mammoth, our ancestor could choose whether to attack it or to flee, but the stressful situations that modern man is faced with are not so easy to react to. In some cases, we may feel that we can only choose between the lesser of two evils: being crushed by a bullying boss or leaving to find a new job, for example. In others, we are unable to react at all to situations that provoke the 'fight or flight' response. For example, when a train is delayed, the commuter waiting for it becomes stressed, but can do nothing to change the situation. The stress inside builds up with no release. The human body, virtually unchanged since the Stone Age, is still adapted (even if it lacks the necessary skills) to hunting mammoths, not to life in the urban jungle. Our physiological development is therefore out of kilter with our technological progress, and modern man is paying for this with the affliction of chronic stress, the pathological effects of which can be deadly.

THE ORIGINS OF THE TERM 'STRESS'

The history of the word 'stress' reflects the relatively recent appearance of this illness. The word comes from the Latin *stringere*, to squeeze, clasp, wound or offend. In Old French this became *estresse*, narrowness or oppression, and modern French has the verb *étreindre*, to embrace or wring, as in wringing one's heart. From *estresse* comes the modern English word *distress*. The use of the word 'stress' to describe a medical condition originated in Britain. The word was first used in the 17th century to denote suffering, deprivation, ordeal or adversity. In the 18th century the word's usage changed. From being regarded as an emotional consequence, stress came to mean a physical cause. In the terminology of metallurgy, 'strain' was used to describe tension in metal, whereas 'stress' meant a pressure that deforms metal. This gave rise, at the end of the 19th century, to its metaphorical use to

**ONE WORD
FOR MANY ILLS**

Suffering, deprivation, adversity ... In the 17th century stress was seen not as an attack on the body, but as the sum of its emotional consequences.

mean psychological stress that could cause physical and mental problems. However, its definition remained vague. 'Stress' was used to describe an attack, a pressure, or a restrictive situation (the term 'stressor' was also used), as well as the body's physiological reaction to these external factors and their damaging effects on health. The interaction between body and soul has always been implicit in the use of the word 'stress'.

A NEW APPROACH TO ILLNESS:
PSYCHOSOMATIC MEDICINE

The idea that life events could have repercussions on an individual's physical and mental health has interested scientists since the beginning of the last century. In 1910 William Osler wrote an article in *The Lancet*, claiming that stress could be the cause of the high incidence of angina pectoris in the Jewish community. This was a new vision in a world of modern medicine. At that time, too, the link between emotional factors and physical illnesses – between psyche (the mind) and soma (the body) – was attracting the interest of specialists in the new discipline of psychoanalysis. In *On the History of an Infantile Neurosis*, Sigmund Freud interpreted the chronic constipation suffered by his famous patient, 'Wolf man', as resulting from repressed homosexuality, which led to the patient's hysterical behaviour. For the first psychoanalysts, such a hysterical neurosis was just one of many manifestations of 'conversion hysteria'. Hard

on the heels of this school of thought came psychosomatic medicine, which was originated in Austria by a contemporary of Freud, Georg Groddeck, who suggested that psychosomatic ailments played a symbolic role. However, this theory was rejected by his successors. According to the best known of these, Franz Alexander, founder of the Chicago school of psychoanalysis, psychosomatic ills were the result of chronic states of nervous tension brought on by unwarranted or inadequately expressed emotions. 'Even a detailed description of the cardiac activity of a patient is worthless if his emotional states and thoughts are not taken into account,' Alexander wrote. He listed seven psychosomatic illnesses that he thought were linked to emotions and thoughts: asthma, ulcerative colitis, peptic ulcer, rheumatoid arthritis, hyperthyroidism, high blood pressure and eczema. Modern it may seem, but this general interpretation of illness, which takes account of the circumstances of life and emotional factors – the 'humours' – is not new. In the second century BC, Galen, one of the founders of modern medicine and of the doctrine of Galenism, asserted that women of melancholic humour were more likely to develop breast cancer than those of sanguine humour. Today, doctors recognise that conditions such as headache, breathlessness and irritable bowel syndrome, as well as the conditions that Alexander listed, may be caused by psychological factors. But before such illnesses could be treated, it was necessary to understand what mechanisms allowed an outside event, recognised by the brain, to actually damage an organ in the body.

SIGMUND FREUD, PIONEER

By proving the link between mind (psyche) and body (soma), the father of psychoanalysis paved the way for psychosomatic medicine.

FIGHT OR FLIGHT

In the 1920s, the US physiologist Walter Cannon studied the fear reactions of a cat in the presence of dogs. He showed that the 'fight-or-flight' response was due to the release into the blood of a hormone produced by the central part (medulla) of the adrenal glands, which are located above each kidney. This hormone, which he named adrenaline, was released in response to nervous stimulation of the adrenal glands. Thus, Cannon had identified the messenger of fear. To confirm his discovery, he injected adrenaline into a cat at rest. The animal's heartbeat and breathing sped up, more blood flowed to its heart and muscles, its fur stood on end, its pupils dilated and its blood sugar level rose – just as if it had seen a dog. Thus, by experimentally reproducing the bodily symptoms of an emotion, the physiologist had proved a biological link between psyche and soma. At the same time, Hans Selye, a young medical student at the University of Prague (he later took Canadian citizenship) noticed that many patients suffering from various infectious diseases showed identical symptoms in the early stages of their illness: shrinking of the lymph nodes, hypertrophy of the adrenal cortex and stomach ulcers. Today, these well-known symptoms are understood to be general signs of stress acting on the body. Selye, who discovered them, called them the 'general illness syndrome' – the body's global, non-specific, organic response to physical attack. Continuing his work as a pathologist, he carried out research into the actions of sex hormones in rats. He was surprised to find that injecting various hormones from cattle into laboratory animals produced the same symptoms as those he saw in his patients who were suffering from illness, serious burns or multiple fractures. Selye then tested the effects of other substances on the rats, such as formalin and water containing impurities, and other kinds of physical damage (X-rays, cold, burns and bruising). No matter what the assault on the system, the rats reacted in a similar way, with a set of non-specific symptoms. In 1936, in an article in *Nature* that has since become famous, he named these symptoms the 'general adaptation syndrome', or GAS. This is the syndrome that today we call 'stress', the body's global reaction to a stressor, though Selye himself did not use this term. Its connotations remained more psychological than biological. Walter Cannon, however, was already talking of the 'stress of excitement' and of 'emotional stress', which he conceived as a response to physical stimuli (low blood sugar levels, cold, lack of oxygen) but equally to emotional stimuli. He also distinguished 'variable stress' (stress of varying duration) from 'fixed stress' (stress occurring at regular intervals), underlining the importance of the length of the ordeal for an individual's reaction. This was a considerable advance. However, it is to Hans Selye that we owe our understanding of the avalanche of physiological processes that leads the body to convert a mental state into a physical reaction. From his work, we know that the increased production of hormones by our bodies when we are stressed can, over a long period of time, lead to physical as well as mental symptoms.

HANS SELYE, FATHER OF STRESS

His great discoveries were the result of observing patients as well as research on rodents.

FROM ANGER TO ULCER: HOW THE NERVOUS SYSTEM AND HORMONES CONVEY THE BRAIN'S ALARM SIGNALS

Hans Selye's work in the following years – encouraged by Walter Cannon and another hormone specialist, Grant Banting, discoverer of insulin and winner of the 1923 Nobel prize for medicine – led to the current definition of stress: the body's reaction to any sharp or sudden variation in the environment, especially when this makes increased demands upon it. This reaction is not just a mass of pathological effects – first and foremost it is an innate physiological means of defence against external stimuli. The body's responses to stress are designed to improve overall performance.

Although Hans Selye is universally regarded as the 'father' of stress, his theory takes no account

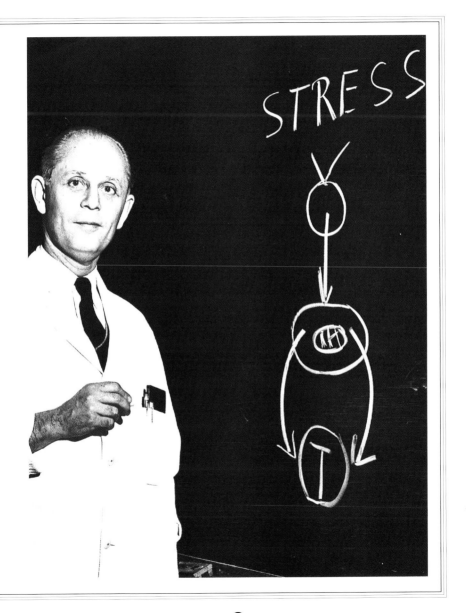

of each individual's characteristics – that is, their ability to cope – or of the context in which an attack occurs. Stress affects people differently. For example, less than 20 per cent of people can act effectively when faced with a crisis such as a flood or fire. Multidisciplinary studies in the wake of Selye's work have shown the importance of this personal dimension in stress, which depends on the individual's psychological makeup, cognitive experience and social and work environment. In order to incorporate all these specific factors, the idea of the general adaptation syndrome evolved towards a 'transactional' model of stress, which was defined from that time onwards as the result of a transaction between the individual and the individual's environment. When this transaction fails, the individual displays pathological responses to stressors. Furthermore, research over the last ten years has thrown light on the complex relationship between the brain, which is the front line in our relationship with stressors, and the immune system, which defends the body against attack from outside or from within. This relationship, which transforms mental suffering into physical illness, involves the nervous system and hormones, which are governed by our particular experiences and our genetic makeup. If a state of stress leads to a stomach ulcer in one person and skin problems in another, this is because the affected organ is made vulnerable by that person's lifestyle, an infection, or their genes. Thus, stressors are manifest in the weakest link in the system. One of the greatest current advances in medicine has been the demonstration of the importance of genetic factors in our susceptibility to stress. Thus, the possession of certain genes can predispose an individual to mental problems such as depression, or physical ones such as high blood pressure or breast cancer – illnesses that are inextricably linked to stress. The more research progresses, the more complex these relations prove to be. But essentially they have remained unchanged since man hunted mammoths.

THE BRAIN: A PROCESSING CENTRE

Our own personal psychological makeup, memory and environment determine our responses to stressful situations.

A BODY POISED FOR ACTION

Let us go back in time. Returning from a hunting expedition, *Homo sapiens* meets a mammoth. Instantly the cerebral cortex of his brain (the grey matter), struck by this terrifying sight – all the more terrifying because his brain's limbic system has stored the memory of earlier confrontations with mammoths – sends an alarm signal to the brain centre that controls many bodily functions. In turn this centre, the hypothalamus, situated at the base of the brain, puts his body on the alert. One of the effects of this message, carried by the sympathetic nervous system, is the release of adrenaline by the central part (medulla) of the adrenal glands and of noradrenaline by the nerve endings. These two hormones are called catecholamines. At the

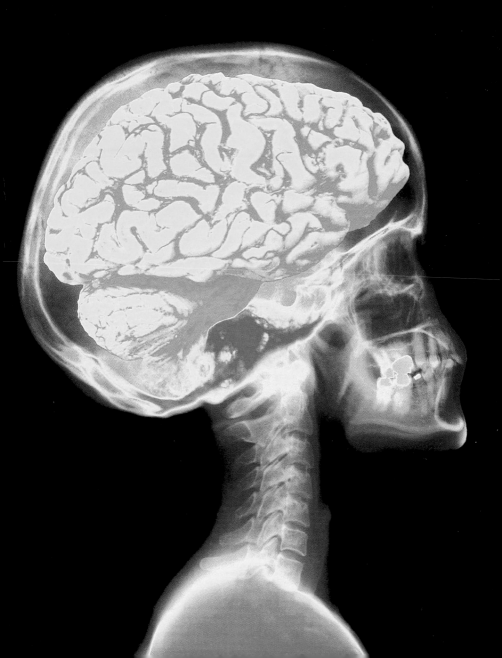

same time, a hormonal messenger, corticotrophin releasing factor, leaves the hypothalamus bound for the pituitary, a small gland at the base of the brain. The pituitary gland relays the message by sending adrenocorticotrophic hormone (ACTH), or corticotrophin, to the cortices of the adrenal glands, making them secrete glucocorticoids such as cortisol. These stress hormones are released very rapidly into the bloodstream, which carries them around the body and puts it into a state of general alert. It takes only a fraction of a second to trigger this unconscious cascade of reactions, but this is enough to transform, almost instantaneously, the body from being at rest into one ready for fight or flight with the muscles and mind ready for action. The stress response provoked by the hormones is designed to increase physical and mental performance. It involves many changes in the major functions of the body, preparing it both for emergency action and for more prolonged effort. The immediate changes are stimulated by adrenaline and noradrenaline. The heartbeat speeds up and the major blood vessels dilate so that they can carry more blood to the brain and muscles in readiness for action. Breathing becomes deeper and faster so that more oxygen can be carried to the muscles, whose tone increases. The pupils dilate to allow more light into the eyes and provide clearer vision. The blood vessels in the skin become narrower, sweating increases and the body hairs stand on end like those of an angry cat. This is an ancient response, and its purpose is probably to frighten an opponent. Thus, the person who is attacked is now ready to do battle or run away, either of which will require the maximum of stamina. The glucocorticoid hormones aid survival in the medium term by increasing the amount of glucose in the blood, thus increasing the amount of energy available to the muscles and brain. They also make the blood clot more readily, minimising bleeding after an injury, and fight allergies and inflammation.

LOOK OUT!

The pupils of our eyes dilate instantly when danger threatens, showing that the brain is on full alert.

COMPLEX PHYSIOLOGICAL REACTIONS
MAXIMISE THE BODY'S RESOURCES

The brain, too, adapts rapidly to danger: the stress hormones secreted by the adrenal glands have a feedback or 'boomerang' effect, acting on the areas of the brain that triggered their release in the first place. Their message could be translated as: 'We are working now: silence the alarm and prepare for action!' This message can be harmful in the long term if the stress is prolonged or too violent. But in the first instance it is highly effective because it awakens the brain and makes it highly lucid, reinforcing decision-making abilities and suppressing feelings that are not needed for immediate action, such as hunger, sleepiness, the sex drive and sensitivity to pain.

Thanks to all this formidable 'machinery', a meeting with a mammoth should not have posed any problem in the prehistoric world. Unfortunately, not all *Homo sapiens* were able to stand up to a mammoth or to run fast enough to escape. Nowadays, dangerous animals are not a major problem anyway. Today, stress-inducers are essentially psychological and so our physiological resources are of little use to fight them. Whether we are dealing with the unpleasant behaviour of a troubled adolescent or with a rush-hour journey on the bus or train, we can often neither fight nor flee. It is largely from this deadlock that the harmful effects of stress arise. Henri Laborit, who promoted the first drug capable of affecting the mind, drew a distinction between psychosomatic illnesses and those due to our inability to act. He realised the benefits of being able to flee from a stressor. Stress is all the more harmful because the brain stores stress attacks in its memory. The glucocorticoid hormones not only

prime us for survival: their boomerang effect on the brain affects the hippocampus (an area of the brain involved in memory and the control of emotions), communicating the biological importance of the stressful event. As a result, each stressful episode is remembered clearly.

This way of sorting the important from the unimportant is essential for survival because it allows danger to be recognised without the need for us to memorise everything. But it has the downside of making the individual remember that in certain situations he or she did not have the means to fight back. For example, in a work meeting, a senior member of staff humiliates a subordinate. The victim is stressed, and his or her body physically prepares itself to react at once by hitting the detractor or by leaving the room, slamming the door. But from the victim's memory come messages of unemployment, unpaid bills, a family to support, and other more deeply buried frustrations and threats.

All these unconscious messages inhibit physical action. The stressed person may relieve their adrenaline overload by 'substitute motor actions', such as drumming their fingers on the table, chewing a pen, twitching their legs, puffing on a cigarette – or they may bottle up their distress or anger, only to vent it later on a subordinate or on their family.

However, such outlets are usually not enough. Victims may then find themselves in the same situation as a rodent trapped in a laboratory experiment, where it is forced to swim continually to stay alive.

AFTER THE CALL TO ARMS, THE FIGHT TO THE END

The following experiment, in which a rat is placed in a desperate situation, shows that a stress reaction can be divided into three phases. The animal is put into a smooth-sided cylinder filled

with water, which forces it to swim and stay afloat to avoid drowning. At first, stimulated by the release of adrenaline, the rat swims energetically. During this alarm phase, known as fear or anguish, its body automatically develops a rapid stress reaction which mobilises all its organs to respond to the sudden demands made on it: the animal's heartbeat and breathing accelerate, its pupils dilate and its fur bristles. But the rat's body cannot withstand this state of general mobilisation for long. The animal then enters the resistance phase, during which it organises its defences: it simply lets itself drift or float, because if it is to go the distance in a continuing stressful situation the animal must save its resources. It delves into its energy stores, notably the sugar reserves in its liver, to increase its endurance. This overrunning of the body interferes with the integrity of many organs and the immune system. This same maladaptive response is also seen in disorders with a psychosomatic component, such as ulcers, asthma, high blood pressure and eczema. Forced to remain in the water, the rat finally enters a phase of exhaustion, in which its body can no longer produce the energy to fight the stressor. The ordeal is too much, and the animal lets itself sink.

THE PRESSURE OF TIME

Even if the task is not urgent, a deadline creates stress because it reduces our control over the situation.

THE PSYCHOLOGY OF CONTROL AND PERCEIVED STRESS

Clearly, everyone does not react in the same way to the same kind of attack. The feelings brought on by reactions to stress vary from person to person: there are fighters and there are defeatists. The difference between them lies in the way a stressor is experienced: that is, the way that perceived information is processed. From the beginning of a confrontation with an aggressor, a constraining situation or a threat, our brain immediately – and unconsciously – makes a double evaluation. The theoretical model for this analysis of information, devised by Lazarus, can be conveyed by two questions: is this stress a danger? And if so, do I have the resources to face it? It is important to understand that the answer to the second question influences the answer to the first. For example, a school pupil who is late feels stressed if he meets a member of staff as he enters the building. Answer to the first question: yes, the stressor is a danger. But the element of surprise, and hence also the stress, is reduced if the pupil has in his pocket a letter from his parents containing an excuse – a means of dealing with the stress – even if he does not show it to the teacher. Being able to control his environment, or merely believing he can, changes his perception of the potential stressor and protects him from its ill effects. The opposite can also happen. Suppose the same pupil has to do a maths exercise that is well within his abilities. His stress level is low. But if he is given a deadline his stress level rises, even if he has enough time, because his control over the situation is reduced. Like

talent for mathematics, this psychology of control is unevenly distributed, for we each have our own way of selecting messages from all those that our environment offers us. Thus, depressed people tend to pay more attention to the negative rather than the positive aspects of a situation, while optimists only see the bright side. People with a low self-esteem may doubt their ability to cope with challenges and may feel that they are not entitled to help with stressful situations. They are therefore more likely to suffer from stress. Some psychologists have identified two main categories of personality: 'internalists', who believe that whatever befalls them depends upon them, their behaviour and their efforts; and 'externalists', convinced that what will be will be, however hard they try to change their destiny. Between these two extremes, of course, lie innumerable intermediate states. However, studies have shown that internalists, certain that they can control a situation, are less susceptible to stress than externalists.

WHEN STRESS CAN HELP

Some people pay no attention to street or workplace noise, and positively enjoy wearing a personal stereo that pumps out decibels at an alarming rate, becoming far less 'personal' as the volume increases. Nevertheless, the ill effects of noise nuisances have been shown quite clearly. Anybody – optimist or fatalist – can be unaware of, or misinterpret, potential stressors such as noise, leading to inappropriate defence reactions. If the source of stress is underestimated, there is a risk of not giving one's best in a trying situation, in the same way that a runner who is indifferent to victory or defeat is not motivated enough to win a race.

NOISE, AN INSIDIOUS STRESS FACTOR

A pneumatic drill is impossible to ignore, but we often under-estimate the nuisance from sounds.

On the other hand, stress can be too intense. If jitteriness before a competition is excessive, the athlete risks losing self-control or finding himself paralysed. In either case, the person's performance is affected. This subjective side to the response to stress depends largely on the complexity of the task to be undertaken. If it is simple, very strong stimulation – that is, a considerable stress – can improve performance. Conversely, a complex task is only carried out efficiently under a minimum of stress.

STRESS FOR GOOD AND BAD

Faced with an attack, a dangerous situation or great psychological or physical demands that threaten the body's inner equilibrium, a counter-reaction is set off to restore that equilibrium. This defence mechanism, which brings the stress reactions into play, produces the symptoms that Selye described when the stressor goes beyond what an individual can withstand. But for

Selye the reaction was the same whatever the stressor. An announcement of mass redundancy is a stressor, but finding out that one has been spared is no less stressful. Because they have the same element of surprise, both pieces of news have the same inner repercussions. But this idea of good and bad stress does not have true scientific value – all the more so because each individual may be able to face stress actively, to make a virtue out of necessity and minimise the effects of the attack and act positively. Thus, a challenge can be a source of anxiety or it can be seen in a positive light. In the latter case, it becomes a stimulant and may lead people to great achievements. There is such a thing as a ferocious will to win. If someone faces a challenge, the control they exercise will give them a feeling of well-being. On the other hand, if they do not succeed in mastering the situation, they will experience failure, or 'distress'.

WHEN STRESS IS EXCESSIVE

The best way to control stress is by the use of specially designed physical exercises, because neuromuscular activity can release inner tensions. In the absence of physical movement, emotions may be put into words, but laughing, crying and screaming are also ways of getting rid of aggressive energy and restoring mental equilibrium. When these are not enough, and especially when the cause of the stress lasts longer than the body can stand, a sense of discomfort and malaise comes over us, an expression of our loss of control over the situation. The physiological stress reaction continues, and the prolonged production of the hormones involved damages not only many of our organs but also the function of our brain. In a normal stress reaction, the hormones act on the brain and cause behavioural adaptations through their boomerang effect. This preparation for action involves the functions of cognition and motivation, the analysis of emotions, memory and sensitivity to pain. Excessive stress on the body's systems may disrupt these brain functions. Prolonged stress can thus be expressed as chronic pain, often with no obvious cause. Overstressed individuals can also find themselves in an over-emotional state: irascible and over-sensitive, they swing between fits of rage and bouts of hysterical laughter, or they may plunge into depression. Very close to this state is that of excessive vigilance, characterised by a stiff demeanour, a repressive attitude to oneself and others, extreme irritability, and often insomnia. Not all stressed people are over-emotional or over-vigilant; some overcompensate and become lost in intense thought or in daydreams, and may suffer from fatigue. Psychological problems can become true illnesses if the cause of stress is permanent or if periods of calm between bouts of stress are not long enough to allow balance to be restored. Stress then turns into anxiety. This happens especially with people under so

THE LIBERATING CRY

When the desire to lash out at everything around us swamps our brain, screaming helps us release and reduce tension.

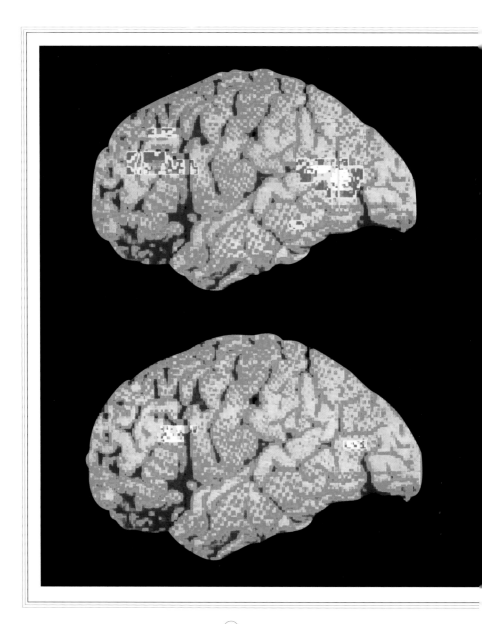

much pressure at work that they are unable to relieve it during their weekends. Overproduction of stress hormones, particularly of corticotrophin releasing factor by the hypothalamus, can cause anorexia, depression, prolonged insomnia, problems with the cognitive processes of memory, and preoccupation with depressive thoughts, all of which can upset concentration. Obsessive–compulsive disorder and panic attacks are also linked to overproduction of corticotrophin releasing factor. Excessive stress may also lead to an increased susceptibility to illnesses such as colds, menstrual problems in women, and impotence in men.

SOME EFFECTS OF STRESS ARE TEMPORARY, OTHERS ARE IRREVERSIBLE AND STARTLINGLY SIMILAR TO AGEING

Chronic stress raises the body's production of corticosteroids permanently. These act on the hormone receptors in the hippocampus, an area of the brain that is essential for memory and the control of our emotions. Faced with permanent stress, these receptors become de-sensitised and memory is impaired. This is followed by the death of some of the neurones (nerve cells) in the hippocampus. Magnetic resonance imaging (MRI) scans have shown that half of all severely depressed patients are affected in this way. The greater the atrophy, the longer the depression lasts. Stress can strike at any age, but anything that diminishes it slows down the ageing process. Conversely, any source of stress speeds up the degeneration that is associated with ageing by increasing the amount of free radicals, which damage DNA and other important molecules in the cells, by a process of oxidation.

In young people, the damage done by stress is reversible if it is due to strong emotions. But the older the individual, the more toxic are the effects of repeated or chronic stress, as the cells of the body become increasingly unable to repair themselves efficiently. An example is the irreversible damage due to stress in people suffering from Alzheimer's disease or arteriosclerosis.

A MOMENT OF TERROR CAN BLIGHT A WHOLE LIFE

All events in which an individual's life is at stake – accidents, terrorist attacks, assaults, natural disasters – can cause the victim, as well as any witnesses, to suffer what psychiatrists call 'post-traumatic stress disorder'. In such situations, the release of neurohormones is so great that the body's whole physiological and psychological balance is upset and becomes impossible to control. Far from being a beneficial adaptation to stress and a readying for fight or flight, the immediate reaction to an extreme stressor can take the form of panic or utter confusion. At the time of the event, or even days later, this acute stress is expressed by dissociation of consciousness and behaviour from reality. The victim does not feel that he or she is 'there': their body is present, but their mind is elsewhere. They may even forget some of what happened. The victim may have the impression of reliving their ordeal in dreams (even waking dreams) and may shun everything that reminds them of the event – including treatment, because this involves talking about it. In some people these disturbances can first appear as much as a month after the event itself. Psychiatrists consider this condition to be chronic if the post-traumatic stress lasts longer than three months. It is not unusual for victims of torture, war or terrorist attack to suffer mental disorders years or even decades after an event, although some people may rapidly get over the same ordeal. Such post-traumatic stress may be linked to genetic factors or to trauma in childhood. It brings with it personality changes (turning inwards, despair, depression, paranoia and phobias) as well as a serious risk of drug- or alcohol-dependency and suicidal tendencies. Although most people do recover given time and treatment, prolonged physical and emotional deprivation may cause lifelong psychological problems.

PHYSICAL ILLNESS INDICATES THE STATE OF MIND

Sadly, the ill effects of intense or prolonged stress do not end there. The list of ailments known as adaptive or inhibitory disorders has grown ever longer since Selye began his work: heart problems, coronary failure, breathing difficulties, muscular spasms, gastroduodenal ulcer, colitis, asthma and other allergy-related illnesses. But while stress is involved in all these troubles, it is never the sole cause. At most it should be seen as a risk factor that makes an illness more likely to appear or to worsen in a person who is predisposed to it, for example by genetic factors, lifestyle or an infection. Thus, an asthmatic may suffer an attack because of a combination of acute anxiety, an allergen and an already allergic constitution. Before making a diagnosis, Hippocrates, a physician who lived in ancient Greece (c. 460–377 BC) and gave his name to the Hippocratic Oath still taken by new doctors, would take into account a patient's constitution: that is, inherited, biological and cultural factors as well as the person's past life and their socio-economic environment and family background. Modern medicine, which formerly regarded such concerns as mere popular beliefs or the province of psychoanalytical theory, is once again taking as much interest in the past experience and personality of patients as in their malfunctioning organs. Two research pioneers of the 1950s, Friedmann and Rosenmann, noticed that many patients who suffered from heart disease had similar personalities and behaviour patterns. Such people, who were constantly racing against time and competing with

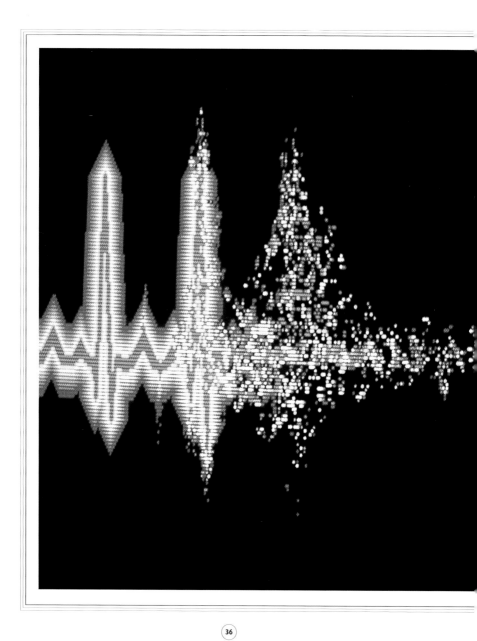

others, were for the most part workaholics who were often carrying out several tasks at once. Ambitious and impatient, they were frequently hostile and agressive as well. Friedmann and Rosenmann believed it would be possible to use behavioural assessment questionnaires to predict which individuals were most at risk of cardiovascular disease – who they termed 'type A' personalities. In the 1990s this theory was thrown into some doubt by a number of broad-based studies (notably the Multiple Risk Factor Intervention Trial, a study carried out on 3,000 people over a period of seven years), the results of which were less conclusive than those of Friedmann and Rosenmann. Nevertheless, these studies highlighted some of the common traits in the psychological profile of heart patients. Among the behavioural characteristics of type A personalities, anger and aggression, expressed openly or otherwise, were seen as indicating a high risk of heart disease. Such behaviour was also associated with early death, from whatever cause. It was also shown that the fewer social contacts a patient had, the higher the risk of death: a single middle-aged man with no close friends had a 50 per cent chance of dying within 15 years, while the figure for a married man with several close friends was 17 per cent. It would seem that talking about problems to relieve stressful situations is a therapy that works.

FATAL FURY

Frequent bursts of anger can make heart attacks more likely.

THE GREATER THE STRESS, THE WEAKER THE BODY'S DEFENCES AND THE GREATER THE DANGER

Each of us knows instinctively that we are at greater risk of succumbing to an infection if we are tired, depressed or overworked. This simple truth illustrates the effect of too much stress on the immune system. The cells that compose this system, which defends us against many harmful organisms and substances, are produced and regulated by various tissues and organs: bone marrow, the thymus, the spleen and the lymph nodes. If there is an attack on the body, the nervous system triggers the release of certain hormones and other chemicals, such as noradrenaline, and in this way the immune system can be depressed by the indirect action of stressors. Experiments on animals have illustrated this reaction, and have highlighted the importance of the 'psychology of control'. If a rat is given repeated electric shocks, it reduces the production of one of the main types of cell of the immune system, the T lymphocyte. On the other hand, if the animal is allowed to control the frequency of the shocks with a lever, or if it can foresee them (for example, if they occur at feeding times), its defence system will not be affected. Here again, the ability to control a situation has a protective effect. The same drop in the number of T lymphocytes can be observed in humans, whether under acute stress (such as school or college examinations) or chronic stress (as might occur when a spouse is affected by an incurable illness such as Alzheimer's disease). Stress is thought to be involved in autoimmune illnesses such as atherosclerosis and rheumatoid arthritis. Its effect on that most tragically notorious of immune disorders, AIDS, has been studied in detail. The results of these studies are contradictory, but a stress management plan for HIV-positive patients has now been developed. It consists largely of combating stress by means of aerobic exercise, which allows the number of T lymphocytes to rise.

DOES STRESS CAUSE CANCER OR MAKE IT MORE LIKELY TO OCCUR?

Deficiency in the immune system is also involved in cancer, in which the body is unable to combat the invasion of an organ by malignant cells. However, the role of stress in cancer remains unclear, partly because there are many types of the disease, but also because the processes of malignancy are still poorly understood. Nevertheless, it is plausible that stress may be at the root of some forms of the illness. One comparative study showed that families in which a child developed cancer had experienced a higher level of stress in the preceding year (from bereavement or unemployment within the family, for example) than families without cancer. Studies of this kind carried out on women who had a malignant lump in the breast (when compared with women who had a benign lump) suggested a similar factor in the development of the disease. However, stress may also aid the progress of cancer or, to be more accurate, reduce the individual's resistance to it. Specialists at a London hospital compared the five-year survival rates of women treated for breast cancer who showed one of

THE WILL TO WIN VERSUS BREAST CANCER
Though cancer is often accompanied by depression, having a strong will to live seems to reduce the risk of relapse.

four attitudes: refusal to submit to the illness, the will to fight it, stoic acceptance, or despair. The rates of survival without a later relapse were higher among those patients who displayed the first two attitudes. In this respect, Galen was indeed right when he rated the chances of 'sanguine' women more highly than those of 'melancholic' women. However, other studies show that the will to fight, or refusal to submit to the disease, can be beneficial, or may have no effect whatsoever, depending on the type of cancer.

The idea that stress plays a role in cancer is partly borne out by the results of psychological testing. This has established that a certain personality type, known as type C, is at a higher risk than others of developing cancer. Type C individuals often appear depressed or hopeless, bottle up their negative feelings, and do not assert themselves or express emotions readily. Between individuals of type A, who are predisposed to heart disease, and type C, who are potential cancer sufferers, lies the full spectrum of responses to stress, which vary among individuals and in relation to various events in life. In the middle of this wide spectrum is the type B individual,

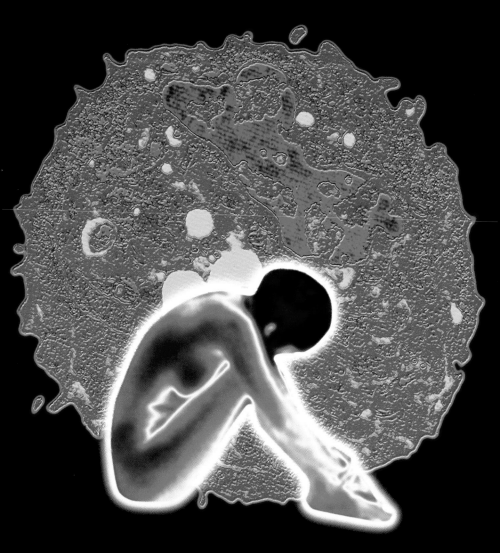

who is neither hostile, nor in a hurry, nor depressed: a balanced individual. Although type B individuals are less likely to develop physical illnesses caused by stress than the other two types, they are still not immune to stress. Very stressful life events can still have harmful effects on them.

THE LANGUAGE OF STRESS

There are many current expressions to describe stress. People talk of being 'fed up', 'bitter', 'exasperated', 'stifled', 'exhausted' or 'having the stuffing knocked out of them'. All these words and expressions describe a condition whose origins and physiological consequences are sometimes obscure, even though it is clear that overwork, worry and distress make people ill. In the 1960s, two doctors, Holmes and Rahe, listed all the life events, great and small, that could cause stress, based on the files of 5,000 patients. They then asked 400 people to mark the importance of these events out of 100, and finally ranked them in order of severity from the most serious (death of spouse = 100) to the mildest (minor legal offence = 11), via moderate stressors such as marriage (which scores 50). A single overall score was then calculated, and was used as an indicator of the true risk of illness. However, it did not take account of the individual's ability to cope with more or less distressing events, or of the personal significance he or she may ascribe to an event. Thus, for various reasons the death of a spouse might be a distressing event for some but come as a relief for others. Neither did the scale allow any room for the small daily worries that taken individually have no detectable effect on health but which cumulatively – even if we pay little attention to them – can become more harmful than a bereavement.

WORK: AN ENDLESS SOURCE OF HIDDEN STRESS

Workplace doctors, ergonomists (who study how people interact with their working environment and equipment) and human resources and personnel departments all work together to eliminate stressors or develop answers to them – though sadly these are not always put into practice. Work stressors are well known. The most common of these are conflicts between people, which are often worsened by managers who apply the principle of 'divide and rule'. There are many others, including the pressure of having to clock on and off; an excessive workload or even not enough work to do; being required to perform repetitive tasks; overqualification, which leads to discontent; underqualification, which causes tension; the possibility of making serious mistakes, and if mistakes are made worrying whether they have been noticed; poor or non-existent job descriptions and the resulting conflicts over people's roles; general uncertainty,

PERSONAL PROFILE

Our reaction to a stress factor depends as much on our past experiences as on the factor itself and its consequences.

LANGUAGE
35

whether from the threat of unemployment or the mood swings of a cyclothymic boss; conflicts over values, such as having to make or sell a product one does not like; responsibility for others' work, because delegation means loss of control; repeated management changes; and an uncomfortable, noisy, poorly lit or polluted workplace... the list is seemingly endless. With so many stressors around, it is hard not to be stressed, frustrated, overworked, anxious or tired at work at some point in life. But workplace stressors are not always where you think they are. For example, bus drivers cope perfectly well with traffic jams because they expect them, but suffer if passengers are hostile. Anyone who works at a bank counter or ticket-office window can be distressed by friction with members of the public, which simple courtesy could avoid. The result is that in all professions many people have the feeling that they live in a permanent state of tension, or 'burnout', as it is known in the USA. According to a recent study by the workplace medical service in France, sales representatives are especially vulnerable: 35 per cent of them suffer from an anxious–depressive syndrome and 8 per cent from a depressive state – often a serious one – and their health deteriorates faster than that of other groups. The typical profile of the sales representative is a married man aged 40, who works 49 hours a week, spends at least one night and eats at least four meals a week away from home, and travels an average of 51,000 kilometres (32,000 miles) a year. However, not all commercial travellers are so vulnerable. According to this study, those who are free to take their own decisions, are supported by their management, believe they have good relations with clients and consider their situation stable suffer the minimum of stress.

JUST A COG IN A MACHINE

Any worker – whether a frustrated employee or an overworked boss – can suffer stress.

A MOTHER'S STRESS WILL AFFECT HER CHILD

There are two factors that can reduce pressure at work. The first is room for manoeuvre – in other words, some autonomy and wide decision-making powers; the second is a low psychological demand on the worker. A US researcher, Robert Karazek, rated the stress risk of various professions based on these two components – control and demand – drawing on a study of 4,500 people. He concluded that it was better to be a researcher than a care assistant or even a doctor, and that the isolation of an architect was preferable to the constant requests made of a switchboard operator. Women, who often have jobs with lower status and lower pay than men, are worst off – all the more because work is not their only source of daily stress. Their environment may also cause problems, particularly if it is noisy, insecure and depressing. Looking after the home, worries over money and the future, lack of time and domestic problems, always weigh more heavily upon women. The typical profile of a stressed individual is a divorced woman about 40 years old, with children and an unrewarding job a long way from home. It is tough on her, but also on her children: child psychiatrists now know how stress on a mother can affect her children adversely, even while they are still in the womb. Babies who are subjected to prolonged prenatal stress are born anxious and below average weight. From the age of three or four, they may become particularly aggressive, be very emotional, suffer disturbed sleep and have difficulty adapting to new conditions. The child's entire system of stress hormones is disturbed, and the resulting damage is probably worse than it would be merely from problems with adaptation. Some US researchers believe that exposing the foetus to the mother's stress hormones can affect the development of many organs, such as the pancreas and the kidneys, as well as the elasticity of the blood vessels. These hormones, which are transmitted to the foetus via the placenta (which can itself be damaged when the mother is under stress) puts its brain into the 'fight-or-flight' state, raising its blood pressure and bringing about other changes. As a result, the child will pay for its mother's stress as it approaches the age of 50, when there will be greater risk of conditions such as high blood pressure, cardiovascular disease and diabetes – and this is without counting the many other stresses that can arise during a lifetime even if the mother is possessed of a Zen-like calm. As these stresses build up, they will increase susceptibility to stressful events and situations, leading the individual to react sooner and more violently to ever smaller stressors. Above a certain threshold – where the person has had enough – the stress reaction gets out of proportion. Some cut themselves off and become very withdrawn, others blow a fuse (experts like to talk of 'kindling', a sort of emotional conflagration). Luckily, something can be done before things come to such a pass.

LOOK

A GALLERY OF IMAGES TO PLEASE THE EYES AND CALM THE SPIRIT.
FORGET YOUR SURROUNDINGS AND THE PRESSURES ON YOU
AND RELAX FOR A MOMENT . . .

Aerial view of sand dunes. *Maranhão, Brazil.*

Mont-blanc, seen from the Grands-Montets cable car platform, France.

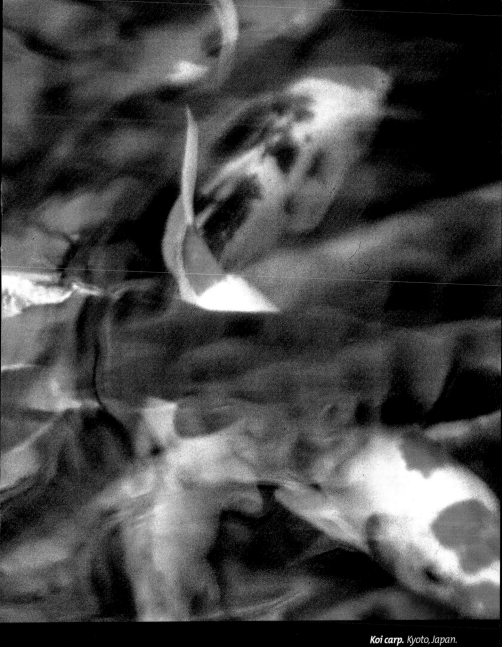

Koi carp. Kyoto, Japan.

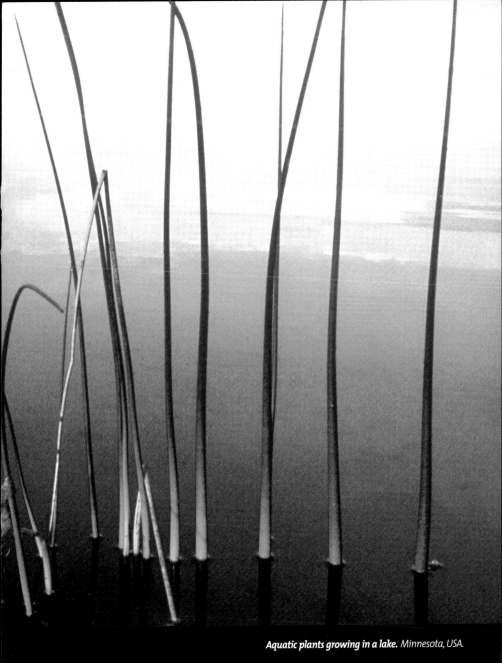

Aquatic plants growing in a lake. Minnesota, USA.

Pine trees in the snow. *Yellowstone National Park, Wyoming, USA.*

Zen garden. *Daisen-In temple, Kyoto, Japan.*

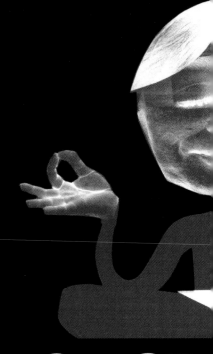

IN PRACTICE

ONCE YOU HAVE RECOGNISED YOUR STRESS, YOU NEED TO MASTER IT.
THERE ARE MANY MORE WAYS OF DOING THIS THAN SIMPLY TAKING
SLEEPING TABLETS AND TRANQUILLIZERS: T'AI CHI, RELAXATION,
HOMEOPATHY, BEHAVIOURAL THERAPY – ALL OF THESE ARE
ALTERNATIVE, GENTLE WAYS OF TAKING ACTION.

The body's response to stress – more than just fight or flight

Faced with a test or a dangerous situation, a specific 'stress response' is set up by the body so that it can react quickly. It all starts in the brain, where physical and mental stress signals are collated and trigger the 'sympathetic nervous system' to fire. This causes the immediate release of adrenaline and noradrenaline (hormones called catecholamines) from the adrenal glands, which are located above the kidneys. These flow throughout the body and put it on maximum alert, ready for battle, by:

• increasing blood pressure
• increasing muscle strength
• increasing mental activity
• increasing the amount of sugar in the blood to provide energy for the muscles

The sum of these effects allows a person to perform far more strenuous physical activity than would otherwise be possible, and is the source of the well-known 'adrenaline rush'. At the same time, the hypothalamus (in the brain) activates the pituitary gland to send a hormone messenger to the outer part of the adrenal glands. These respond by releasing large amounts of another stress hormone, called cortisol (a glucocorticoid), which intensifies the adrenaline rush and helps to maintain the response.

These physiological processes help the body and mind to cope with stressful events, and the effect is a positive one. However, this effect may become harmful if it is prolonged (for example, long-term stress is linked to high blood pressure), and so it is important to be in control of your level of stress.

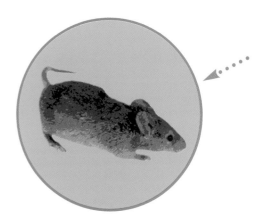

WHEN WE ARE FACED WITH AN UNWELCOME SITUATION, THE BODY'S ALARM SYSTEM MOBILISES THE STRESS CIRCUITRY.

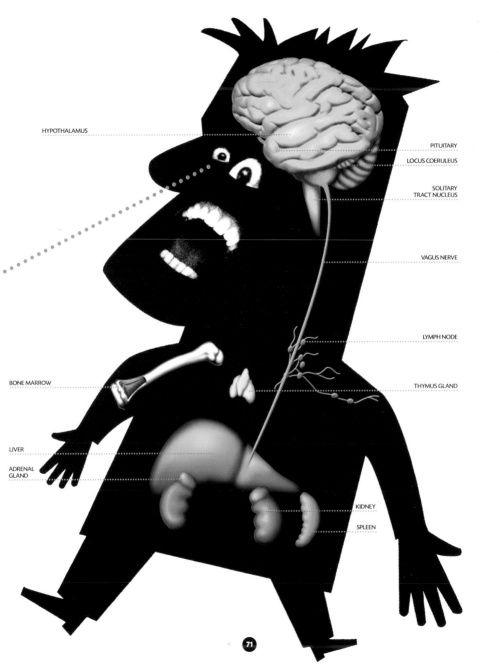

HYPOTHALAMUS

PITUITARY

LOCUS COERULEUS

SOLITARY
TRACT NUCLEUS

VAGUS NERVE

LYMPH NODE

BONE MARROW

THYMUS GLAND

LIVER

ADRENAL
GLAND

KIDNEY

SPLEEN

Stressed or unstressed?

Stress and its effects on us are subjective, personal elements in our lives. We do not all perceive the causes of stress in the same way. Our bodies are physiologically able to react to small worries as well as serious threats, and in many people this reaction lasts barely longer than the event itself. But in others, who are more sensitive to stress, the disturbance lingers – often unknown to them – and so they feel stressed.

Flush out the guilty parties!
Self-assessment on its own is not enough. The opinions of those around you, your own state of health, your timetable – all these are indicators of your level of stress. Once you are aware of this, you will still need to identify your main stressors before you can know whether, and how, you can change them. Once you have done this, you may be able to devote more time to stress-relieving activities, or perhaps you will master stress management techniques such as relaxation, assertiveness and cognitive therapy. Nothing is beyond hope.

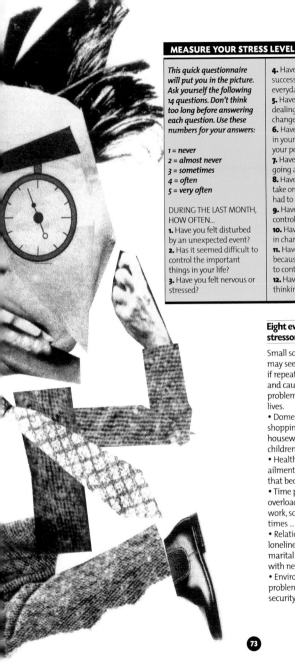

MEASURE YOUR STRESS LEVEL

This quick questionnaire will put you in the picture. Ask yourself the following 14 questions. Don't think too long before answering each question. Use these numbers for your answers:

1 = never
2 = almost never
3 = sometimes
4 = often
5 = very often

DURING THE LAST MONTH, HOW OFTEN...
1. Have you felt disturbed by an unexpected event?
2. Has it seemed difficult to control the important things in your life?
3. Have you felt nervous or stressed?

4. Have you dealt successfully with small everyday problems?
5. Have you felt you were dealing effectively with big changes in your life?
6. Have you had confidence in your ability to handle your personal problems?
7. Have you felt things were going as you wanted?
8. Have you felt you could take on all the things you had to do?
9. Have you been able to control your irritation?
10. Have you felt you were in charge of a situation?
11. Have you felt angry because you were not able to control events?
12. Have you caught yourself thinking about things you

were supposed to have achieved already?
13. Have you been able to control how you spend your time?
14. Have you felt that difficulties were piling up so much that you could not control them?

For questions 1, 2, 3, 8, 11, 12 and 14, score 1 for if you answered 1, 2 if you answered 2, and so on. For the other questions score 1 if you answered 5, 2 if you answered 4, and so on. The closer your total score is to 70, the more important the rest of this book is for you.

After Cohen and Williamson. Adaptation: Pascal Quintard.

Eight everyday stressors

Small sources of stress may seem harmless, but if repeated they pile up and cause serious problems that can poison lives.
• Domestic worries: shopping, cooking, housework, looking after children ...
• Health problems: minor ailments, fleeting pains that become chronic ...
• Time pressure: an overloaded timetable at work, school hours, train times ...
• Relationship problems: loneliness, adolescence, marital rows, arguments with neighbours ...
• Environmental problems: noise, lack of security, pollution ...
• Money worries: cash-flow problems, loan repayments, heavy debts ...
• Work worries: deadlines, bullying, frustration, an incompetent boss ...
• Worry about the future: unemployment, doubts about retirement, your children's work prospects ...

Social Readjustment Rating Scale

Holmes and Rahe devised this scale in 1967. It rates the most common causes of stress in a person's life on a scale of 1–100.

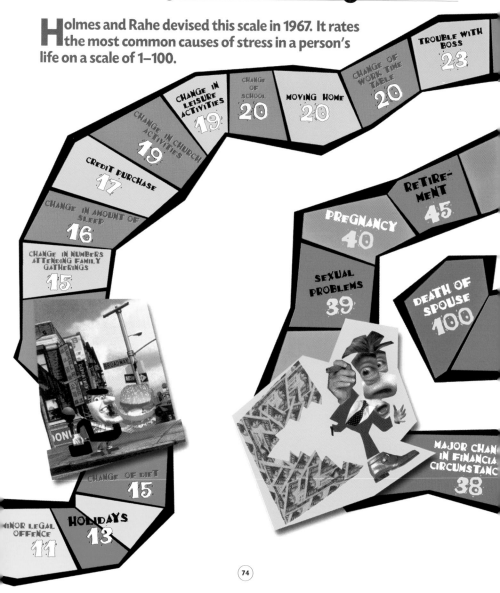

TROUBLE WITH BOSS
23

CHANGE OF WORK TIME TABLE
20

MOVING HOME
20

CHANGE OF SCHOOL
20

CHANGE IN LEISURE ACTIVITIES
19

CHANGE IN CHURCH ACTIVITIES
19

CREDIT PURCHASE
17

CHANGE IN AMOUNT OF SLEEP
16

CHANGE IN NUMBERS ATTENDING FAMILY GATHERINGS
15

RETIRE-MENT
45

PREGNANCY
40

SEXUAL PROBLEMS
39

DEATH OF SPOUSE
100

MAJOR CHANGE IN FINANCIAL CIRCUMSTANCE
38

CHANGE OF DIET
15

HOLIDAYS
13

MINOR LEGAL OFFENCE
11

MAJOR CHANGE IN LIVING CONDITIONS
29

OUTSTANDING PERSONAL SUCCESS
28

PROBLEMS WITH IN-LAWS
29

CHILD LEAVING HOME
29

CHANGE IN WORK DUTIES
29

RECONCILIATION WITH PARTNER OR SPOUSE
45

LOSS OF JOB
47

MARRIAGE
50

SERIOUS ACCIDENT OR ILLNESS
53

ASSET SEIZED
30

DEATH OF CLOSE RELATIVE
63

TAKING OUT A MORTGAGE
31

DIVORCE
73

SEPARATION FROM SPOUSE
65

IMPRISON-MENT
63

EATH OF LOSE FRIEND
37

CHANGE OF JOB
36

CHANGE IN RELATIONS WITH SPOUSE
35

A day in the life of a victim of stress

A likely sufferer would be female, fortyish, a single parent, doing an unfulfilling job and living far from her workplace. At 6.30 a.m. the alarm clock goes off after a restless night spent on a worn-out bed; she is woken by street noise and neighbours coming home late. So starts the hellish daily race. Jump out of bed and throw together breakfast for the family. A quick visit to the bathroom – the mirror pitilessly shows up rings round her eyes, grey skin, drawn features, lank hair ... Starting the day is tough for Sue – aged 40, divorced with two children – who works as a cashier in a London department store. Quickly she pulls on the outfit she laid out the previous night.

Make-up will have to wait until she's on the train. From now on she is on the treadmill: wake up the two children, dress them, give them their breakfast, make sure they brush their teeth, and get them off to school. Sue drops them there and races to the station. Every minute of her timetable is accounted for. On the train she meets friends, jokes, puts on make-up, perfume ... now she is dressed for work. Then 40 minutes of what almost amounts to rest, despite the other passengers, the closeness of the atmosphere, the noise. The rest of the day will be without respite: being nice – or trying to be nice – to hurried, barely polite customers. During her half-hour lunch break Sue quickly munches a sandwich brought from home and gets in some shopping.

Work is over: now it's time for the children

At 6.00 p.m. it's time to go home: the same race in reverse. Once there, the children take priority: there's homework to supervise, washing, arguments ... After dinner, when the table has been cleared, it's the children's bedtime. Sue is alone at last but exhausted ... and there's still the ironing to do. Never mind, she'll do it tomorrow. She sits down in front of the television but her eyelids are drooping, so at 10.00 p.m. it's lights out. But in bed sleep eludes her. Her head is spinning: it's the end of the month and money is tight ... Holidays? She daren't even dream about them. Roll on Saturday!

Get rid of those false friends!

Caffeine, tobacco, alcohol, cannabis – some people come to rely on these drugs to provide relief from stress. The temporary effects may seem helpful, but there is a high price to pay for the fleeting sense of well-being.

Caffeine – fast-acting, long-acting

Caffeine is found in coffee, tea, chocolate and cola, and has a stimulant effect on all the organs in the body. Although it relieves tiredness, it increases the release of the stress hormones adrenaline and noradrenaline. These act to raise the heart rate and blood pressure. Anything more than three cups of coffee a day may cause irritability, overstimulation, and anxiety, thereby compounding stress. Caffeine reaches its peak concentration in the bloodstream between 30 and 60 minutes after absorption, but even ten hours later enough of it can remain to have a small effect. This can lead to insomnia and make fatigue worse.

Nicotine – a highly addictive drug

About 13 million people in the UK smoke regularly. Tobacco contains nicotine, a fast-acting drug that acts as a tranquilliser and also increases the heart rate, raises blood pressure, and stimulates the brain. Possible ill-effects of smoking include cancer and heart disease.

Alcohol

Some people regard alcohol as a harmless tonic. Alcohol does reduce anxiety and tension through its depressant effect on the brain. However, regularly drinking alcohol to relieve stress is likely to lead to alcohol dependence or regular consumption of large amounts. Alcohol interrupts sleep patterns, and regular abuse can cause personality changes, mental problems, depression, and liver and heart disease.

Cannabis

Legal drugs such as alcohol are not the only problem. The last decade or so has seen a steep rise in the use of cannabis, especially among 15- to 25-year-olds. Because marijuana, grass or dope, obtained from hemp *Cannabis sativa*, produces relaxation and a sense of well-being, some people use it to relieve stress. It is not addictive, but it can lead to permanent apathy. If it is smoked with tobacco, the harmful effects of the tobacco pose an extra health risk.

Work – a false escape

To get away from the stress of family or a difficult relationship, for example, some people take extreme measures, such as throwing themselves headlong into their work.

But overloading yourself like this and ignoring the fundamental problem is no solution: it simply stores up trouble. Stress accumulates, and physical or mental collapse may be just round the corner.

Give your body a break

Even if you are under stress because you have little opportunity for physical activities, it is not advisable to fling yourself into too much strenuous sport when the opportunity does arise. There is no point in adding muscular or back problems to an already stressful situation.

Put your stress to good use

Any stressful situation can be turned to your advantage: instead of letting it upset you, you can face it and draw benefit from it.

Stress can help you cope better

Stress in itself is not an illness, nor is experiencing it a sign of weakness. It is a normal bodily response whose function is to stimulate the system, making it easier to adapt to a changing environment. As we have evolved, it has greatly increased and modified our capacity to adapt, so that we are better able to face threats from the natural world and from man-made dangers like revolution and war: it has allowed us to be what we are. Everyday life is not a competition, but it is as well to act as if it

were, for there is no achievement without stress. Managed properly, stress stimulates us. But we do not all perceive messages from our environment in the same way and we are not all equally sensitive to threats; faced with the same hazard, people react differently.

How to make stress work for you

The way each person faces stress and deals with it is crucial. Coping strategies, which can be constantly refined and improved, teach us to face stress without becoming indifferent to it, so that instead of being distressed by the demands made on us we make allies of them, turning them to our advantage.

The simplest example is a traffic jam. There you are, stuck on the ring road or motorway. The signs that warn of delays do not help, even though they make the situation more controllable by telling you how long the delay is. You're going to be late, and you cannot curb your racing pulse, the knot in your stomach, your growing impatience ... One solution would be to park your car and walk the rest of the way. Another, more positive response would be to listen to music, to try to relax, and to use this time alone to think about other matters and the things that please you. In short, detach yourself from what you cannot control in order to be better able to deal with the rest of the day.

If you are not to join the ranks of the pathologically stressed, you must keep your stress reactions down to a level that allows you to give your best when conditions are good while limiting damage as far as possible when things get difficult. When coping strategies alone are not enough, you must seek help, if possible from friends, relatives, support organisations or professionals. Above all, change your circumstances as much as you can.

Managing your own stress

Social life, love life and work always involve stress. You might as well learn to live with it and prevent it from ruining your life.

Change the way you think

The basic rules for managing stress are the same for everyone, but you still need to devise a personal strategy. Each individual has to find what suits them and works for them in the long term. Not everyone can make radical changes in their life, but you can learn to make things easier by devising your own plan to control stress. First of all, you must pinpoint the source (or sources) of your stress. You can do this by keeping a stress notebook, rather like the notes about eating habits that patients who are trying

to slim make for their dietician. Record every event, big or small, that upsets you during the course of the day, such as a stab in the back by a colleague or a marital row. You should also record the emotion you experienced (such as anger or anxiety), the thoughts that occurred to you (for example, 'it always happens to me') and how you behaved (eg going for a walk or shouting at someone close to you). Having established where you stand, you should go on the attack – not all at once, but step by step, as problems arise. Start by making an effort to think differently: you may not be able to change your environment, but you can change the way you see it. Did you argue with your spouse or partner this morning? Forget that row, live in the present, concentrate on your work, and in the evening take some flowers home for them. Do traffic jams irritate you? Distance yourself from them, and use your enforced inactivity to listen to good music or perhaps a 'talking book', or make plans for the future.

Putting things in perspective, living in the present, distancing yourself and changing the images in your mind: such active strategies, though simple, are often enough to lower your level of stress. It was strategies like this that the US psychiatrist Aaron Beck used in developing an accessible form of stress treatment based on common sense, called cognitive therapy: become aware of the thoughts that come to you automatically, such as 'I'll never succeed' or 'people don't care', and then challenge them, stressing the positive rather than the negative.

Dare to be selfish

Managing your own stress also means using relaxation techniques, learning to say 'no' calmly, and delegating to others duties that have become a constant worry. Change your appearance: give yourself a new image by eliminating grey and black from your wardrobe – such changes can be a first step towards ridding yourself of debilitating stress. Allowing yourself a small treat every day can give you positive feelings that work against stress. And finally, why not dare to be selfish without feeling guilty, even if it goes against everything you have been taught? This can only be to your advantage. So treat yourself, let yourself go.

Lead a healthier life

Managing your stress also means checking how healthy your lifestyle is. The watchword is 'balance', but don't forget to enjoy yourself! Just do it sensibly.

There is no healthy mind without a healthy body. If your system is to fight stressors efficiently, you must follow a few common-sense rules. The first is to eat a balanced diet. Increase your intake of raw foods and eat less cooked food; eat more vegetable fats and fewer animal fats. Natural dietary fibres (found in wholemeal bread, fruit and vegetables) help food to pass through the intestines and reduce the amount of fat that is absorbed into the bloodstream. Choose fish (oily or otherwise) and poultry over fatty red meats or salami; this will reduce the risk of obesity, certain cancers and – above all – heart disease. Eat plenty of complex carbohydrates (bread, pasta, brown rice, lentils, beans) but cut down on simple carbohydrates such as sweets and pastries. Cut down on dairy products too, as the digestive system of an adult human is not well suited for handling milk, especially cow's milk. In addition, cut down on alcohol in all its forms and in order to reduce your risk of high blood pressure you should eat less salt .

Find the right sport for you

For good measure, take regular, moderate exercise. We have all noticed how we feel calmer and more relaxed after exercising. Research has found a physiological explanation for this. During physical effort the sympathetic nervous system is activated so as to deal appropriately with the physiological stress that is caused. When our exercise ends, the parasympathetic nervous system acts to restore our physiological balance by setting off a series of responses that oppose the stress reaction. The feeling of relaxation after a long period of exercise is also due to the secretion of endorphins, natural opiate-like substances that give a sense of euphoria, a natural 'high'. Choose your sport according to your abilities, your tastes, your timetable – and do it at a regular time. Do not set your sights too high: you will not be able to run a mile on your first outing. Start with 20 minutes of walking or gentle gym exercises three times a week rather than an hour and a half of sit-ups, buttock muscle exercises and stretching. Using your muscles is good for your body, but it's good for your mind too. It uses up the fatty acids that are released into the bloodstream by stress hormones, preventing these acids from clogging up the arteries, helping the blood flow back to the heart during hard work, and minimising any increase in blood pressure.

The siesta makes a comeback

Sleep replenishes your physical and mental resources. Try to sleep if you feel you are going off the rails, but without using sleeping pills. Invest in a good bed, shut out noise from your bedroom, remove the television and avoid heavy dinners and coffee just before bedtime. Learn to relax. Why not bring back the afternoon siesta? Although daytime sleeping is not advisable for those who suffer from insomnia, it allows the rest of us to 'decompress' and to recharge our batteries. After lunch (without coffee), 15 minutes rest in an armchair is enough, either in the office or at home. This will perk you up for the rest of the day. A crafty siesta will reduce stress too.

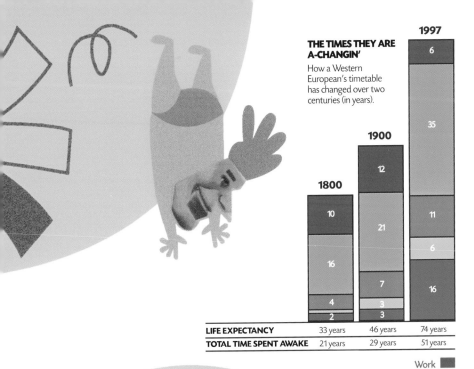

THE TIMES THEY ARE A-CHANGIN'

How a Western European's timetable has changed over two centuries (in years).

1800

- 10
- 16
- 4
- 2

1900

- 12
- 21
- 7
- 3
- 3

1997

- 6
- 35
- 11
- 6
- 16

	1800	1900	1997
LIFE EXPECTANCY	33 years	46 years	74 years
TOTAL TIME SPENT AWAKE	21 years	29 years	51 years

Work

Resting

Education

Travel

Leisure

Source: Francoscopie, Editions Larousse, 1999.

Learning to relax

You can learn to make yourself relax. Whatever method you use, after a period of relaxation you should be mentally alert, your muscles loose, not tense, and your mind relieved of all worry.

There are many paths to relaxation

Relaxation counteracts the harmful effects of stress. There are many ways to achieve it, and they have long proved effective in treating stress-related ailments such as headaches, insomnia and aches and pains. The Schultz method, also called 'autogenic training', was developed at the beginning of the 20th century by Johannes Heinrich Schultz. The patient lies down in a comfortable position, arms and legs loose, and tries to feel as if he or she is sinking into the ground, starting with an arm or

foot and then gradually extending this feeling to the rest of the body. To this feeling of heaviness the patient must then add the sensation of warmth, and this localised relaxation then spreads throughout the body. Having passed this milestone, the patient concentrates on their heartbeat, breathing, the solar plexus, and finally on the face, upon which they imagine a gentle, fresh breeze is playing. It takes several sessions to learn to get through all these stages. The training process is rather long – at least two sessions a day at home and one a week with a therapist – but results show that the technique is effective.

T'ai chi ch'uan

Though gentle and serene in appearance, t'ai chi ch'uan is a martial art. Records of it go back to the 12th century, and the discipline contains elements from the Buddhist and Taoist traditions. The essential goals of its practitioners are 'joy of the spirit' and 'peace of the heart'. These spiritual qualities are intimately linked to the body, to breathing and to health. Training consists of repeating simple movements, which are then combined in more complex sequences to make up 'the form'. The pace and simplicity of the basic moves makes this seem easy at first. For beginners, training focuses on learning and memorising the sequences and the correct patterns of movement. These are a series of fighting moves performed one after the other in time to slow, regular breathing. This martial art is practised in groups outdoors, in order to connect with nature's 'vital force'. Training takes place indoors, to improve comfort and concentration.

RAPID RELAXATION

In the office or at home, find a quiet place and sit in comfort for a few minutes. Relax, keeping quite still. Listen to your natural rhythm of breathing and be aware that you are exhaling automatically; each time you exhale relax a little more and loosen the rest of your body. Repeat the exercise several times a day, and your stress will decrease. Once your body is relaxed, ideally you should go to sleep. If you do these exercises during the day and need to resume an activity after relaxing, you can restore tone to your muscles by breathing hard while clenching your fists, stretching, and screwing up your face.

Don't suffer in silence – a trouble shared is a trouble halved

Brooding in a corner, alone with your problems, is no solution. The stressed person feels the weight of the world on their shoulders, but help can be very close at hand, simply in the form of friends, relatives and neighbours – a trouble shared with them is a trouble halved.

Many experts believe that one of the best cures for stress and problems is other people! Forcing yourself to make contact with them, talking to neighbours and local shopkeepers is a real step forward. Make use of those around you – tell them about the events of the day or the week that have left a bitter taste in your mouth, the problems you have been unable to resolve or rid from your mind in spite of having chewed them over and over.

Faith heals

Religion can help some people out of a crisis. Attending church, synagogue, temple or mosque can be a way of reducing stress. Several studies in English-speaking countries have shown that practising believers have a lower risk of stress affecting them.

Keep your social ties alive

Other people's suggestions or opinions can throw new light on a situation and help you find the germ of a solution. Social relations are vital in brightening our lives, but they may break down when too much stress swamps us and we take refuge in drink or drugs. Don't lose sight of the fact that you are not alone in your sorrow or stress and that other people may be able to offer useful help and advice.

When we have reached this stage it can be hard to talk to those close to us, who must bear the brunt of our distress. So don't be afraid to contact groups such as Alcoholics Anonymous and support groups for former smokers or ex-drug addicts, where you can speak to others who are suffering or have suffered in the same way. Having experienced the same or similar problems themselves, members of these organisations are living proof that you can overcome your problems and get through difficult times. It is in forums such as these that we can share our experiences and our pain. For some people, stress manifests itself as an illness or a phobia, such as agoraphobia, claustrophobia, or fear of water, flying, or other people. These conditions can be treated by meeting with former sufferers, or by teams of professionals who specialise in helping people overcome such fears.

Acupuncture and hypnosis

Acupuncture, auricular therapy (a form of acupuncture stimulating points on the ear) and hypnosis bring relief to stress sufferers who are wary of other treatments.

Acupuncture, an integral part of Chinese medicine, is an ancient method of treatment that has been adopted enthusiastically in the West. It takes account of the relationships people have with their environment, the climate, the seasons, and even the rays that emanate from the sun, the moon, and the earth upon which we live. Acupuncture is based upon two ideas. The first is that of energy or *chi*, which governs the universe and its reflection – man. This energy exists in two alternative and complementary forms: yang, which is positive, and yin, which is negative.

The second fundamental idea is that stimulation of specific sites on the skin influences the function of certain of the body's systems or organs. These sites, called 'acupuncture points', are located along lines known as 'meridians', which are the channels along which the body's vital energy flows. It is believed that illness and stress disturb the balanced flow of energy, and that appropriate stimulation of the acupuncture points along these meridians will regulate the energy flow to restore good health and relieve the effects of stress.

Hypnosis

Many general practitioners and psychiatrists turn to hypnosis in order to help patients seeking relief from their troubles, especially from stress. To be hypnotised, the patient must concentrate on an image, a sensation or a memory so as to reach a state of trance, rather like sitting in traffic and thinking of something else. Once the patient is both comfortable and relaxed, the therapist asks him or her to seek the cause or causes of their stress, with the aim of teaching them to control the situation rather than simply to suffer it. Hypnosis does not work every time, or with every patient, but five to ten sessions can often achieve quite remarkable results.

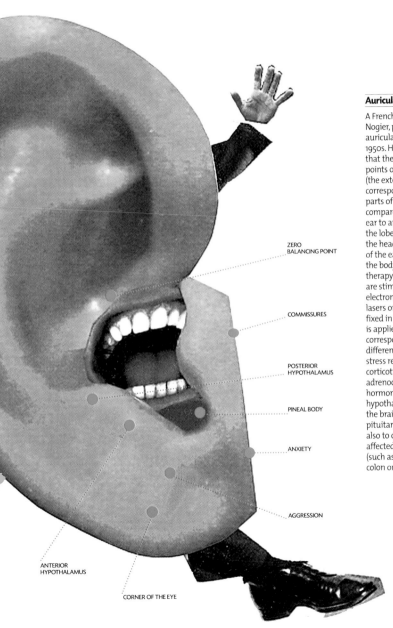

ZERO
BALANCING POINT

COMMISSURES

POSTERIOR
HYPOTHALAMUS

PINEAL BODY

ANXIETY

AGGRESSION

ANTERIOR
HYPOTHALAMUS

CORNER OF THE EYE

Auricular therapy

A French doctor, Paul
Nogier, popularised
auricular therapy in the
1950s. He maintained
that there is a series of
points on the auricle
(the external ear) that
correspond to different
parts of the body. He
compared the external
ear to an inverted foetus,
the lobe representing
the head and the rest
of the ear representing
the body. In auricular
therapy these points
are stimulated with
electromagnetic currents,
lasers or pins which are
fixed in place. Treatment
is applied to points
corresponding to
different aspects of the
stress reaction –
corticotropin (ACTH or
adrenocorticotropic
hormone), the
hypothalamus (part of
the brain) and the
pituitary gland – and
also to organs that are
affected only indirectly
(such as the stomach,
colon or skin).

Behavioural, cognitive and psychoanalytical therapies

Learning to think differently, changing your behaviour and discovering your motives can all contribute to the management of stress and help you rise above it. Such steps can work successfully together.

Every therapy involves a therapist. The stress sufferer is not alone with his or her troubles – someone else will be working with them on how best to deal with these problems and reduce stress. If the first therapist you go to does not suit you, you should not regard this as a failure. Keep trying until you find one with whom you feel comfortable—there is no point in adding stressful therapy to your problems. The aim of therapy is to boost the patient's self-confidence and sense of control over their life, thus decreasing their stress reaction. The patient must then systematically identify and critically examine their stressful (or even depressive) thoughts or cognitive processes, so as to be able to question them and defuse them.

Change your behaviour

Behaviour such as losing your temper or raising your voice is often a symptom of stress. But it can also be a cause, as when someone does not dare express an opinion or, on the contrary, flares up over a trifle. In such cases the therapist and patient work together to change the patient's behaviour. The patient learns to behave in new ways when stress is felt to be increasing – distancing himself or herself from a stressful situation, slowing down, smiling, or indulging in a treat ...

Yo're talking absolute Rubbish

1. Group sessions with one or two therapists are used to examine the way people relate to each other (their social skills) – for example, asking for something, saying 'no', expressing or receiving criticism, starting or interrupting a conversation, or talking about emotions. In this way the members of the group learn to change their behaviour and attempt to draw all sources of stress out of their daily lives. At the end of the session, each patient takes away a list of things to do when stress occurs. At the next session, patients give each other a rundown of what has worked and what hasn't.

2. Stress Inoculation Training (SIT): developed by Donald Meichenbaum, a Canadian psychologist, this is a complete stress management programme that combines cognitive therapy with other methods of combating stress. Initially the therapist helps the patient analyse his or her situation by distinguishing stressors (such as the environment or thoughts) from their reactions to them (cognitive, behavioural or physiological processes).

Once the patient has become aware of these problems, the therapist teaches him or her to face each problem by the use of coping strategies centred on the problem and its associated emotions, and this allows the patient to rediscover ways of adapting. Next, skills are learned and practised: the patient imagines that the source of stress is present, so that he or she can recreate the problem and become aware of the symptoms. The patient then tries to master the symptoms, using the skills that have been learned, until the situation no longer causes stress and he or she can behave in such a way as to resolve the problem. After this re-enactment, the patient can put into practice what has been learned, both in role-playing with the therapist and in reality. When stress is only the tip of the iceberg and it is not enough just to change bad habits, the patient's distress needs to be explored further by working on the subconscious mind, seeking out memories of the past. Psychotherapy or psychoanalysis can be of great help in this.

Antidepressants and other drugs prescribed for stress

With about 15% of the population on antidepressants and anti-anxiety drugs, the British rank among the world's biggest consumers, and women are the biggest users.

Psychoactive drugs act on various chemical transmitters in the brain that are released in response to stress. They are available only on prescription and should be used with caution.

Benzodiazepines

This group of drugs was developed in the 1950s and is used for the treatment of severe anxiety. The drugs slow mental activity by reducing the signals between brain cells. This reduces agitation and makes you feel relaxed. There are many different kinds on the market, differing chiefly in how long they are active. Properly prescribed, benzodiazepines act quickly and effectively. They have only a low level of toxicity and few side-effects as long as they are used in small doses for no longer than two weeks. But they commonly cause drowsiness, and for this reason they are often used as sleeping drugs. They can also cause confusion, dizziness, and lethargy. Drinking alcohol while taking benzodiazepines is dangerous because it increases the sedative effect. Taking the drugs for longer than two to three weeks may lead to dependence, and stopping the treatment after this time may cause withdrawal symptoms such as excessive anxiety and insomnia.

	Days of antidepressant treatment prescribed per 1000 inhabitants in 1997	Change from 1992 to 1997
Belgium	40.32	+ 10.8 %
France	39.65	+ 3.8 %
Great Britain	32.37	+ 13.8 %
Germany	22.37	+ 12.3 %
Spain	22.23	+ 16.1 %
Netherlands	17.99	+ 13.4 %
Italy	11.54	+ 5.3 %

Source: SmithKline-Beecham Laboratories, 1998

Antidepressants

Although these drugs are designed to treat depression, they may be used to treat the feelings of anxiety that result from too much stress. The most commonly used antidepressants, selective serotonin reuptake inhibitors (SSRIs), can be used in the treatment of panic attacks and phobias. There is no risk of addiction, but they take at least ten days to have an effect and may cause diarrhoea, vomiting, reduced sex drive, and headache.

Sleeping tablets

These drugs restore sleep patterns that may be disturbed by stress. There are many different types available, and some containing antihistamines are available without prescription. However, you should always consult your doctor before starting to take sleeping drugs. Although they can relieve insomnia, sleeping drugs do not treat the cause, which may be stress, anxiety, or fear.

Beta-blockers

Beta-blockers are widely used to treat diseases of the heart and circulation. Some of them may also be prescribed to control the physical symptoms of stress and anxiety. The drugs block the action of the stress hormones adrenaline and noradrenaline, thus suppressing symptoms such as palpitations, sweating, clammy hands and trembling. This reduces anxiety and helps sufferers appear more self-assured. The drugs can be effective against nerves on a big occasion, such as a job interview, but need to be taken several hours before. The drugs can cause disturbed sleep, cold hands and impotence, and should not be taken by people with asthma.

Alternative treatments

Stress can be treated by means other than conventional drugs. Other medicines are available, usually without prescription, to which you can turn when stress becomes hard to manage.

Homeopathic medicine is based on the principle that the symptoms of illness or stress we experience are the body's natural way of restoring its balance, or 'homeostasis'. Homeopathic remedies are chosen for their ability to mimic these symptoms when taken in large doses, but because only minute doses are actually given, the effect is simply to stimulate the body's natural defences.

Homeopathy treats people who suffer from stress according to their personal profile: the practitioner adapts the treatment to the patient. For example, a type A person – impatient, overachieving, hyperactive, ambitious and aggressive – would be prescribed Argentum nitricum, Aurum metallicum, Nux vomica, Platina, Sulfur and Tuberculinum. However, a type B patient, who is adaptable, copes with stressful events, responds to challenges and welcomes change, would be given Lycopodium, Clavatum, Nux vomica, Sepia and Sulfur.

Plant treatments and trace elements

Treatment with plant remedies offers gentle, alternative therapy. Hawthorn, passion flower, valerian, *Escholtzia californica*, St John's wort or ginseng, taken in drops or pastilles three times a day, can work wonders.

Taking trace elements, such as magnesium or calcium, can often bring a little relief. Like plant products, they are used to treat particular symptoms of stress, such as irritability, nervousness, tetany and spasms. Trace elements are usually taken as tablets, capsules or powders.

Flower treatments

Bach flower remedies – 38 essential essences – are taken in drops as required, as often as every quarter of an hour if necessary. Each essence is aimed at a particular disorder. There are also ready-to-use mixtures of essences. One of these, specific to stress, mixes elixir of verbena, oak, impatiens, agrimony, white chestnut, pine and wild apple.

Alexander technique

The mental and physical habits we acquire as we go through life can result in mental problems such as anxiety, as well as a variety of aches and pains. The Alexander technique is a way of correcting these habits. Under the guidance of a trained teacher, you learn to 're-educate' your mind and body so as to improve your freedom and ease of movement, balance, support, coordination and sense of well-being.

Ayurvedic medicine

In Ayurvedic medicine, a proper balance of body, mind and spirit is maintained by adjustment to ways of thought, diet and lifestyle, and use of herbal treatments.

Autonomy, the secret of relaxation at work

Enjoying autonomy at work reduces psychological pressure and, indirectly, stress. The more an employee is in charge of his or her work, the less they are under pressure and stress, and the more they can enjoy life.

A study of 4,495 people, conducted in 1989 by the US researcher Robert Karazek, showed that two factors – autonomy (in other words being able to act independently) and psychological pressure from the work environment – were decisive in determining how much stress people suffered.

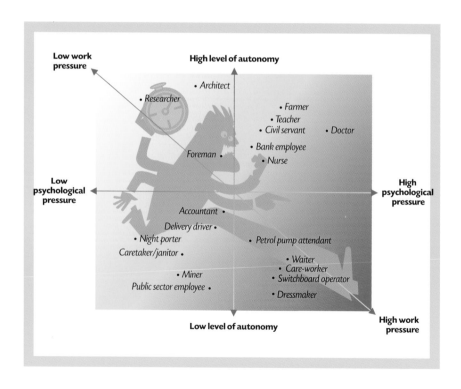

FIND OUT

MANY MODERN WRITERS DEAL WITH STRESS IN THEIR WORK.
FIND OUT WHAT TYPE OF STRESS SUFFERER YOU ARE. SIMPLE,
HELPFUL TRUTHS AND 40 GOLDEN RULES FOR BEATING STRESS.
USEFUL ADDRESSES TO HELP YOU FIND MORE INFORMATION
OR SOMEONE TO TALK TO.

Therapy
David Lodge

An 'ideal' and well-adjusted life can bring its own stress. In this intimate confession by a teacher in his fifties, a mere pain in the knee makes him realise that his sad, deadly dull existence is gnawing away at him.

The first time I felt the pain was about a year ago. I was leaving the London flat, hurrying to catch the 18.10 from Euston ... when I felt it: a sharp, piercing pain, like a red-hot needle thrust into the inside of the right knee and then withdrawn, leaving a quickly fading afterburn. I uttered a sharp, surprised cry and keeled over on to the bed (I was in the bedroom at the time). 'Christ!' I said, aloud, although I was alone. 'What the fuck was that?' ...

About a week later, when I was working in my study, I crossed my legs underneath the desk, and I felt it again, the sudden stab of pain on the inside of the right knee, which made me gasp, sucking in a lungful of air and then expelling it with a resounding 'Fuuuuckinell!' From then onwards I began to get the pain with increasing frequency, though there was nothing predictable about it. ... It would make me cry out in the middle of the night, so that Sally thought I was having a nightmare. In fact nightmares are about the only thing I don't have, in that line. I have depression, anxiety, panic attacks, night sweats, insomnia, but not nightmares. I never did dream much. Which simply means, I understand, that I don't remember my dreams, because we dream all the time we're asleep, so they say ...

I felt it was a bit hard that I should get a mysterious pain in the knee on top of all my other problems. Admittedly, there are worse things that can happen to you, physically. For instance: cancer, multiple sclerosis, motor neurone disease, emphysema, Alzheimer's and AIDS. Not to mention the things you can be born with, like muscular dystrophy, cerebral palsy, haemophilia and epilepsy. Not to mention war, pestilence and famine. Funny how knowing that doesn't make the pain in your knee any easier to bear ...

I went to my GP first. He recommended physiotherapy. After a while, the physiotherapist recommended that I see a consultant. The consultant recommended an arthroscopy. That's a new kind of hi-tech microsurgery ...

It's a year since my arthroscopy, and I'm still getting pain. Should I risk another operation? I don't know. I can't decide. I can't make a decision about anything these days. I couldn't decide what tie to wear this morning. If I can't make a decision about a little thing like a tie, how can I make my mind up about an operation?

...I have a lot of therapy. On Mondays I see Roland the physiotherapist, on Tuesdays I see Alexandra for cognitive behaviour therapy, and on Fridays I have either aromatherapy or acupuncture. Wednesdays and Thursdays I'm usually in London, but then I see Amy, which is a sort of therapy too, I suppose ...

Early on in my treatment Alexandra told me to take a sheet of paper and write down a list of all the good things about my life in one column and all the bad things in another. Under the 'Good' column I wrote:

1. Professionally successful
2. Well-off
3. Good health
4. Stable marriage
5. Kids successfully launched in adult life
6. Nice house
7. Great car
8. As many holidays as I want

Under the 'Bad' column I wrote just one thing:
1. Feel unhappy most of the time

A few weeks later I added another item:
2. Pain in the knee

© David Lodge 1995. Secker and Warburg

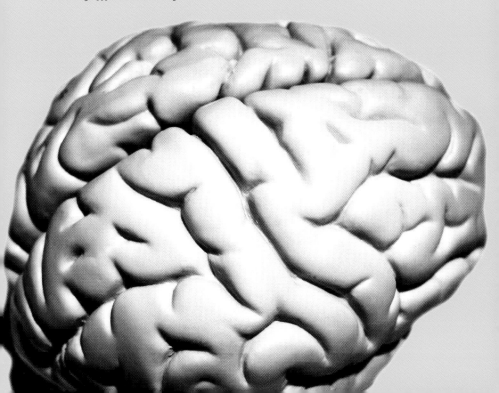

Eureka Street
Robert McLiam Wilson

A street in Belfast, Northern Ireland. For 75 years everything has conspired to make it a paradise ... of stress. Terrorism is a constant threat, civil war a daily experience. Wretchedness has become inseparable from Ulster's identity. Half the population suffers from religious discrimination. Thirty per cent of Catholics are unemployed, but only 18 per cent of protestants. Yet in this chaos, life goes on.

Anyway, Ronnie was running the show and he would have been impossible to stop. He was like a new man. He buzzed and fizzed with surplus energy. Even I had to concede that it was fairly impressive for a man in his fifties. He worked at double pace and barked at these unfortunate women with something like real hunger. During the lunch break, someone had asked him what he was on and Ronnie had explained to us all.

He had been suffering from chronic insomnia for some years. He attributed it to the Anglo-Irish Agreement and the creeping suspicion that his country would soon be in the hands of the filthy Roman Catholic Church. Never having had a day's illness in his life – something always claimed by fascists, for some reason – he had visited his doctor with some reluctance. The doctor had refused to prescribe sleeping pills. He had told Ronnie that there was a new Californian technique, which sounded absurd but worked like a charm. He advised Ronnie to think nice, soothing thoughts in bed to calm him and lull him into sleep. Nothing about sex or work or money. Pleasant green-trees kind of stuff.

Ronnie took the doctor at his word and tried the technique. For weeks it had not worked. No sylvan musings seemed to help Ronnie sleep. Then he decided to personalise the process.

Broadening the conflict
Michel Houellebecq

A dynamic young manager has plenty of sources of stress in his life. But the root of his distress is not necessarily where one might think. It isn't overwork that is pushing him to the brink, but rather his sordid, lonely life.

After the meal he wanted to have a drink in a 'nice bar'. Great idea ... We sat down and he ordered a bourbon and water. I stuck with beer. I looked around and thought: this is it; this could be the end of the road for my unlucky friend.

We were in a student café: everyone was jolly, out to have fun. There were several tables with two or three girls sitting at them; there were even some girls alone at the bar ... This was the time to pick one up: here, at this precise moment, in the perfect place to do it.

He looked up from his drink and fixed his gaze on me from behind his spectacles. And I realised that he no longer had the strength. He couldn't do it; he hadn't the nerve to try; he was completely sick of it all. As he looked at me his face trembled slightly. It was probably the drink: he'd had too much wine at lunch, the idiot. I wondered whether he was going to burst into a fit of sobbing and tell me the stages of his own personal Calvary. I was expecting something of the sort: his spectacles were slightly fogged with tears.

That was not a problem: I was ready to take it on, to listen to everything, escort him back to the hotel if necessary – but I knew he would resent me for it next morning.

I kept quiet and waited in silence, for I really couldn't think of anything sensible to say. He wavered for a good minute, and then the crisis passed. In a strangely weak, almost bleating voice he said: 'We'd better go home. We've got an early start in the morning.'

Fine, let's go home. We'll finish our drinks and go. I lit a final cigarette and looked at Tisserand once more. He looked utterly haggard. Without a word he let me pay; silently he followed me to the door. He was stooped, shrunken, ashamed of himself, despising himself. He wished he was dead. We walked towards the hotel. In the street it began to rain. So that was the end of our first day in Rouen. And I knew, with the certainty born of experience, that the days to come would be unwaveringly identical.

What kind of stress sufferer are you?

Two people might resemble each other on the surface, but prove utterly different when faced with a crisis. Their reactions depend on their response to stress. Stress sufferers can be divided into three categories – types A, B and C. The following test will tell you which type you belong to.

For each statement that applies to you, turn to the box 'How to mark your answers' on page 106 and make a note of the category – A, B or C – that corresponds to this statement. If a statement does not apply to you, do nothing. The results will be explained later.

1. You never have enough time to do all you would like to do.

2. When driving, you do your best to hold back and always try not to be aggressive.

3. You can't bear taking decisions on impulse, without weighing up the pros and cons.

4. You quickly become irritated by someone who beats about the bush without getting to the point.

5. You find it difficult to show your emotions, and it's even harder to express them in words.

6. It is vital for you to cultivate your own private, secure space.

7. You sometimes dream of revenge for all the injustices you have suffered.

8. You can't bear wasting time.

9. You are glad when people laugh, even if they are laughing at you.

10. When driving you never retaliate, but force yourself to keep quiet even if you're livid inside.

11. For you, a day without some small pleasure or treat is pointless.

12. If someone insults you when you're driving, you won't let the matter rest; you won't let anyone else have the last word as a matter of principle.

13. You assume that new acquaintances will become your friends.

14. If one of your work projects fails you feel so humiliated that you wouldn't wish to relive the experience at any cost.

15. If you have to act urgently, you always take a moment to weigh up the pros and cons.

16. You can't bear the thought of being retired one day.

17. You hate doing several things at once, because you know you won't be able to do any of them to your satisfaction.

18. Career and money are a means to happiness, but you don't want them to become priorities.

19. You are sometimes troubled for days on end by a small worry you should have been able to forget quickly.

20. You have difficulty delegating at work: you fear your colleagues could take your place or – worse – make you appear dispensable.

21. Daily worries are inevitable. You try to put them in perspective so that you can ignore them.

22. You don't know how to say no, and you suffer as a result.

23. Some people are born to lead, others to be led: such is life. You are one of the leaders.

24. When your companions laugh, your first thought is that they are making fun of you, and this makes you uneasy.

25. Competition brings out the best in you.

26. If you fail in a project at work you are not downhearted – you feel you will know how to handle things better next time.

27. You are annoyed when you don't know why your companions are laughing.

28. You hate drawing attention to yourself.

29. If you were given more responsibility you could really prove your worth.

30. You get more satisfaction out of giving than receiving.

31. You blush easily.

32. If you are forced to rest you soon become restless.

33. You hate having to compete because you are sure you will lose.

34. You often work hard until the last minute before going home, because this makes you perform better.

What your result means

HOW TO MARK YOUR ANSWERS

1. A / 2. B / 3. C / 4. A / 5. C / 6. B / 7. C /
8. A / 9. B / 10. C / 11. B / 12. A / 13. B /
14. C / 15. B / 16. A / 17. C / 18. B / 19. C /
20. A / 21. B / 22. C / 23. A / 24. C / 25. A /
26. B / 27. A / 28. C / 29. A / 30. B / 31. C /
32. A / 33. C / 34. A

Type A profile

Driven, hyperactive, hurried, impatient: all these describe a type A person. Someone who is always in a hurry – their diary is packed and they rush around all day. For a type A person, a minor incident can turn into a drama. Don't push in front of them or take their parking space! Type As are perfectionists, and they are hard on themselves. They have difficulty delegating and trusting others because they see themselves as indispensable, even irreplaceable. They can be polite, even pleasant, as long as nothing gets in their way. But if you try to outshine them or put one over on them they will fly off the handle, and the competitive beast within will take over.

HOW TYPE A FUNCTIONS

Type A people are born of a highly competitive society that encourages them to continue in their ways. They are admired for their authoritarianism, and it's their force of personality that makes them a winner. And why should they drop their guard for an instant? Within family or business, the type A person meets little opposition and nobody tries to restrain them. Being with other people allows them to indulge in a little verbal jousting or to test their authority. For this reason, solitude and idleness often terrify a type A. They rule out relaxation in any form, and often view retirement as a tragedy.

ILLNESSES

Type A individuals are susceptible to acute stress with strong bursts of adrenaline, which affect the heart and blood vessels in the long term. Their intense lifestyle is often accompanied by high levels of cholesterol and fats; they may be overweight or have latent or actual diabetes, and many of them are smokers. Type A men and women are therefore thought to be at higher risk then others of high blood pressure, heart attacks, angina and ulcers.

TREATMENT

Type A individuals have no choice but to take time out. They have to force themselves to do this, because overwork is built into their temperament. They should distance themselves and take an interest in other things – the joy of spending time with their family, for example. It is a tough task, but type A people are usually highly adaptable because of their alert state, caused by the adrenaline they secrete.

Type B profile

Falling between types A and C, this second category is not so much a type as an ideal blend. Those who enjoy this well-balanced type of personality, whose calm is as exemplary as their self-control, are comparatively rare. Some people are born type Bs, but more often than not they become type B through their own efforts, having learned to manage the situations they encounter.

HOW TYPE B FUNCTIONS

The key is balance. Type B individuals achieve a good balance between self-respect and respect for others. Having nothing to prove to anybody, they live in harmony and suffer less stress. Interest in other people takes precedence over self-pity.

ILLNESSES

Type B people generally enjoy good health. Because they control themselves better, they also control the secretion of their hormones, and consequently suffer less from stress-related psychosomatic illness. In theory, this is the best guarantee of a long life!

TREATMENT

There is no need to retire to an ashram to achieve this state of grace. It is enough to be self-aware each day and to learn to control yourself quickly when minor incidents occur. Let things go rather than convince yourself that they are worth getting annoyed about. To live happily and in good health, we should all be type Bs. Not easy, but well worth trying.

Type C profile

Men and women of this type are introverts, often unable to release their emotions. As a result they keep everything inside and rarely communicate their state of mind. Because of this they often take the role of the unloved, sitting in a corner on their own – so much so that type As and Bs might wonder whether they aren't enjoying it a little.

In life and at work, the perfect antithesis to the type C is the type A. Unlike type As, type Cs hate pushing themselves forward, testing themselves against others, competing. At work, they would rather be static than improvise. Because they lack self-confidence and take it as read that their ideas are bad, they keep themselves to themselves. As well as the typical type C personality just described, there is the 'false C'. This is a kind of fall-back position sometimes adopted by repressed individuals of type A. If a type A person is prevented from asserting his or her true self, perhaps because circumstances force them to suppress their authoritarianism, they will behave like a type C. But inside they are seething, and at the first opportunity they will let fly at the unlucky people who happen to be near them. For example, a type A person thwarted in his or her professional life may behave like a type C. But at home they take on their type A character once again, and their nearest and dearest pay the price of their daily frustration.

HOW TYPE C FUNCTIONS

People rarely become type Cs. In general they are naturally inclined towards this type of personality, or at least predisposed to it. Education does the rest: it can either help a young type C to come out of their shell or drive them more firmly into it. Pure type Cs are, in general, poorly treated by society, which prefers type As. They are not very assertive and find themselves torn between what they want and the fear of getting it. Their desire for just recognition is often gagged by the fear of being exposed. Above all, they are characterised by inhibition and paralysis. Paralysis can be total if the person cannot escape from pressures or deal with confrontations.

The type C individual is naturally disposed to falling victim to all that society holds to be taboo, as well as to things that are condemned by his or her subconscious: good food and drink, perhaps, or sexual enjoyment and indolence.

ILLNESSES

Their internal contradictions render type Cs especially vulnerable to chronic stress. Their behaviour is especially harmful, because failing to react to an attack on the system is extremely destructive. Type Cs feel under attack but do not react because they can not or will not, even if they know they have good reason or a pretext to do so. When we take constant punishment without flinching, the body secretes large quantities of the hormone cortisol, and this leads to disruption of the system that regulates this hormone. It is now thought that many illnesses are linked to chronic over secretion of cortisol. For example, people who suffer from depression have been found to secrete more cortisol than others; equally, their immune system is weakened. The negative attitude of type C individuals is thought to lead to a general slowing down of the body's systems, low blood pressure, a slow pulse and a variety of illnesses.

TREATMENT

A true C can never become an A. But they can endeavour to let themselves go, to express themselves, above all to say 'me', 'I' or 'no'. Type Cs need to learn to respect and believe in themselves. Since they have a strong tendency to devalue themselves, those around them should help them by encouraging them in what they do.

Simple truths that can help you

All behaviourists, whatever their school of thought, agree that self-persuasion is beneficial. These brief thoughts are based on the method developed by Emile Coué (1857–1926), a French doctor who is perhaps best known for advising his patients to tell themselves, 'Every day and in every way, I am getting better and better.'

After all, I've still got time to improve and become stronger.
Winners are made, not born.

I will succeed, I can do it.

I have the situation under control. That's what matters.

I have good qualities – I just need to learn to make better use of them.

I'm not the type to give up when the going gets tough.

When I compare myself with others I have nothing to be ashamed about really.
Anyway, some people would be only too glad to be in my shoes.

Every defeat is merely a delay.

It's within my reach: no problem.

If it doesn't work today, it will tomorrow, or the day after.

I have nothing to lose and everything to gain.

40 golden rules to beat stress

1 Choose the priorities that are right for you and decide what is really important.

2 Don't worry: it's pointless!

3 Don't brood on a failure or disappointment.

4 Tell yourself that everyone makes mistakes or suffers setbacks sometimes; nothing is ever insuperable.

5 Shut out unrealistic thoughts.

6 Question yourself whenever necessary.

7 Clarify a situation as soon as possible, so that misunderstandings never become entrenched.

8 When things really go wrong, say to yourself: 'I'm in a bad way because ...' Identify the causes of stress so that you can tackle them.

9 Listen to those around you.

10 Learn to say 'no' to unpleasant or even distressing things, even if you are unsure of what the consequences may be.

11 Enjoy yourself and stimulate your mind – games, outings, reading, following the news, meeting people, etc.

12 Every time you feel bad, go out and see people rather than retreating into yourself and your stress.

13 Give yourself at least one small pleasure every day, however simple – buy something, eat something nice, listen to a favourite song, pamper yourself ...

14 Reward yourself for positive thoughts and actions.

15 Set yourself achievable targets every day.

16 Don't be hard on yourself.

17 Instead of blaming yourself, look for the real causes of a failure.

18 Avoid negative or unpleasant thoughts; don't brood on them pointlessly.

19 If a problem looks big, don't just keep thinking and worrying about it: write it down and draw up a practical strategy to resolve it.

20 Each time you catch yourself becoming angry or irritable, ask yourself whether it's really worth it.

21 Keep a diary where you record all the good things that happen to you, and talk about it often with a friend.

22 Try to draw up a list of your three best qualities, and always keep it with you.

23 Always have something to look forward to in the short or medium term – an outing or holiday, a book or article to read, an invitation ...

24 Adopt a good posture. Stand with your feet slightly apart so you feel stable. When sitting, use all the chair to settle yourself firmly, with your back against the backrest. Always hold yourself straight, with your shoulders back, look whoever you are talking to in the eye, and avoid unnecessary gestures.

25 Help yourself to relax by smiling and laughing.

26 Hum or sing whenever you feel like it – in the street, on public transport, doing chores ... This will help lighten your mood.

27 Follow your natural rhythm of sleep, waking, resting and eating.

28 Try to breathe deeply when you feel under stress.

29 Correct yourself when you catch yourself in a tense position – clenched jaw, clenched fists, knitted brows ...

30 Walk in a green space or in a street lined with trees, and try to think of nothing.

31 Set aside at least a few minutes every day for relaxation of some sort – breathing exercises, meditation, yoga, bathing in essential oils ...

32 Take regular, moderate exercise.

33 Take control of your diet (eat what you need, at the right time).

34 Eat under ideal conditions (in a quiet place, sitting down, unhurriedly).

35 Do not neglect your appearance – look after your body, choose clothes carefully.

36 Surround yourself with bright, positive colours, and avoid negative ones such as black and grey.

37 Furnish your home attractively, so that you can look forward to going back there in the evening.

38 Tell the person you live with of your problems as soon as the occasion arises, without waiting for things to get worse, but don't burden them.

39 Find places that make you feel good and go there often.

40 Put your troubles in perspective and don't bemoan your fate.

How to eat for a stress-free day

Not everyone's life can be so well-organised that their diet is always perfect. However, the very act of cooking a meal can be part of your anti-stress programme: what you eat and how you prepare it can affect your physical and mental state. Even choosing and handling the ingredients can be a pleasurable, sensual experience. Your choice of dishes is important: a diet rich in fibre, fruit and fresh vegetables favours relaxation of mind and body. On the other hand, too rich a diet leads to problems with circulation and digestion. Ideally you should eat at regular times, in peace and quiet, taking plenty of time over it. Sit down and enjoy your meal – don't wolf it down.

Grilled chicken salad with curry sauce

For two people:
2 skinless chicken breasts, 2 teaspoons sesame oil, 1 teaspoon freshly chopped rosemary, 1 teaspoon curry powder, 1 teaspoon mustard, 100 ml (3 fl oz) mayonnaise, salt, pepper, mixed salad leaves and a few cherry tomatoes.

Preheat the grill to a medium temperature, brush the chicken breasts with the oil, and season with rosemary, salt and pepper. Grill for seven minutes on each side. Leave to cool. Mix the mayonnaise with the mustard and curry powder to make a curry sauce. Lay the leaves on the plates, put the chicken breasts on top of them, garnish with the tomatoes and serve cold with the curry sauce.

Carrot cake

Serves eight:
200 ml (7 fl oz) oil, 125 g (4 oz) brown sugar, 100 ml (3 fl oz) honey, 350 ml (12 fl oz) milk (soya milk if possible), 700 g (1 lb) wholemeal flour, 2 teaspoons baking powder, 1 teaspoon salt, 1 teaspoon cinnamon powder, 1 teaspoon nutmeg, 225 g (8 oz) grated carrot and 100 g (3 oz) chopped nuts.
For the icing: grated rind of half a lemon, 3 to 4 tablespoons of icing sugar, 3 tablespoons of lemon juice and 100 ml (3 fl oz) hot water.

Preheat the oven to gas mark 4/180°C. Whisk the oil, sugar, honey and milk, together until light. Add the flour, baking powder, salt, spices, carrots and nuts. Pour the mixture into a greased 25 cm (10 in) cake tin. Bake for around 50 minutes until golden, and leave to cool before turning out. To prepare the icing, beat the icing sugar, water, grated lemon rind and juice and leave to cool before spreading it over the top of the cooled cake.

Breakfast
• Tea or herbal tea, with little or no sugar and no milk (to rehydrate the body).
• Fromage frais or yogurt, with kiwi fruit or sweetened with honey (provides calcium).
• Buttered wholemeal bread or muffin (provides fibre, complex carbohydrates and vitamin A).

Lunch
• Mixed salad: lettuce, hard cheese (cheddar, Gruyère or Emmental), nuts, hard-boiled egg.
• Grilled chicken breast with slice of lemon (provides protein and vitamin C).
• Moderate helping (50–100 g, 2–4 oz) of rice or pasta (a complex carbohydrate).
• Orange (rich source of vitamin C).

Afternoon
• Fruit, or fruit and vegetable juice (such as carrot and celery; contains beta-carotene and sodium).

Dinner
• Fish, eg sea bream (low in fat), baked in foil (without fat).
• Steamed vegetables (steaming helps to preserve the vitamins) and baked potato.
• Fruit salad (pineapple, apple, berries, peaches, banana; avoid oranges as their high vitamin C content can interfere with sleep).
• A small piece of plain chocolate can raise your spirits!

A feelgood cocktail

For one glass:
4 carrots, 4 leaves of spinach, 4 sprigs of parsley and 2 sticks of celery.

Wash and cube the carrots. Put the celery, spinach and parsley in a blender and blend to a juice. Add the carrots and blend again.

Vegetarian lasagne

For two people:
90 g (3 oz) blanched and drained spinach, 150 g (5 oz) crumbled tofu, a small chopped courgette, half a pepper cut into thin strips, olive oil, salt, pepper, 500 g (18 oz) tomato sauce, three sheets of cooked, drained lasagne, 60 g (2 oz) grated Gruyère cheese and 1 tablespoon grated parmesan cheese.

Preheat the oven to gas mark 4/180°C. Brown the pepper and courgette in the oil. Mash the spinach and mix it with the tofu, and season well with salt and pepper. Oil a baking dish and spread a thick layer of tomato sauce, a sheet of lasagne, half the spinach and tofu mixture and half the courgette and pepper, and sprinkle on half the Gruyère. Repeat to make another layer, then sprinkle the parmesan on top. Bake for 45–55 minutes.

Aromatherapy – a cocktail of fragrances

For people under long-term stress, therapy and good intentions are only part of what's needed. Here are some simple daily activities that will encourage the body and mind to rid themselves of stressful habits.

Self-massage, a home-made blessing

You don't need to turn to a specialist for your first emergency measures against stress. You can get by very well at home. With or without essential oils, a few simple movements will fit the bill.

• **Your body**: Using the tips of your fingers, start at the nape of your neck, and make circular movements towards your collarbones down to your armpits, and then finally up and down your legs.

• **Your hands**: Massage the palm with the thumb and the back of the hand with the fingers with a pressing, circular motion.

• **Your feet:** Using both thumbs, massage your feet from the toes to the ankle. Then massage each toe in turn, from the base to the tip.

• **Your face**: To finish, tap your face with your fingertips, then massage it from the centre of the forehead to the temples. Gently squeeze your eyebrows lengthways between finger and thumb, and do the same with your mouth. Make circular movements with your fingers from your cheekbones towards your ears. Finally, place your hands on your neck and move them one after the other up to your chin.

ST JOHN'S WORT

A well-known antidepressant, this plant is prescribed four times as often as conventional drugs in Germany. In the UK it is available in tablet form from health food shops and pharmacies. In March 2000 the government issued an urgent health warning as recent research has indicated that St John's wort can reduce the effectiveness of certain prescription drugs including the contraceptive pill, drugs used to suppress the HIV virus, some heart drugs and medication used to treat epilepsy and asthma. Therefore always consult a doctor before you take it.

Essential oils are natural remedies and can be used in various ways. They can be massaged into the face, added to bath water, used under the shower, or you can simply fill a room with their fragrance. First choose a base oil, and then add precise amounts of plant essence. The doses needed for each application are as follows:

Massage: two drops of each essence per 30 ml (10 fl oz) of base oil. Never use neat essence alone without diluting it.

Face: one drop of each essence per 15 ml (5 fl oz) of base oil.

Bath: four drops of each essence per teaspoon of bath oil.

Shower: two drops of each essence per tablespoon of shower soap.

Ambience: three drops of each essence per teaspoon of base oil.

Nervous tension: lavender and roots of vetiver or camomile and rose. Massage into the solar plexus, inhale, or add to bath water.

Anxiety: basil and sage or roots of vetiver and lavender. Rub into the wrists or solar plexus, or inhale.

Fatigue or low energy: juniper and lemon or rosemary and geranium. Massage all over the body or add to bath water.

Depression: basil and sage or marjoram and ylang ylang. Rub into the wrists, temples and solar plexus, inhale, or add to bath.

Migraine: peppermint and camomile or lavender and rosemary. Rub into the wrists, inhale, or add to bath water.

Stop brooding

As well as all the little joys, daily life involves a mass of minor events and worries that sap your energy. Between them, they make your mind work flat out.

We are always thinking – even if our bodies take a rest from time to time, our minds don't. We never pause for breath, and bit by bit our life is swamped by a thousand worries. At night, our head is so full that we can't get to sleep.

The best way to break the cycle is to do something absorbing that enables you to forget everything else. Ideally, this should be a manual but non-repetitive activity, which captures your attention and doesn't leave a second for thinking about the Inland Revenue, what you'll be doing on Saturday night or money worries. During this time you will be so involved you will forget all your cares. You should find that when you come back to your daily concerns you can view them with detachment, at least for a few minutes. Manual activity like this also allows you to recover your concentration, which is so often lost under prolonged stress. In the Middle Ages, monks were obliged to spend part of each day illuminating or copying manuscripts and part of the day gardening. In this way they alternated intense manual activity with intellectual work, and we would do well to follow their example. Think how the colouring in that children love to do improves their concentration.

As a change from repetitive, monotonous mental or physical work we can turn to pastimes. These are far from being frivolous ways of killing time when we have nothing better to do – quite the opposite. Hobbies can be rewarding and enjoyable, and offer a complete break from the routine of work and family concerns. There are dozens of activities you could try – here are just a few.

Embroidery

Once the pastime of idle noblewomen, embroidery has made a comeback as a hobby for busy businesswomen. It is easy to carry about with you on the train or between meetings and occupies your mind, leaving no room for worries, which you can firmly put off until later.

Painting

You don't have to be an artist to wield a paintbrush! A true artist suffers for his art, but an amateur paints for pleasure – and it can work well as a stress-reliever, giving you an outlet for the pressures suffered through the day.

DIY

The image that springs to mind may be of tools and overalls, but DIY can almost rise to the level of art if you are designing a cosy interior. And it is doubly beneficial, because you will be occupying yourself and making your home a more pleasant place at the same time.

Jigsaw puzzles

The smaller the pieces, the better. What could be more absorbing than reconstructing a large print of Monet's *Waterlilies* from 2,000 tiny fragments, each almost identical to the naked eye? You need patience – and lots of it – to succeed!

Model-making

Like embroidery, this involves great precision. Producing a scale model from hundreds of small parts and a tube of glue must count as the stress-busting pastime par excellence.

Role-playing games

Developed in the 1970s in the USA, role-playing games were revolutionary because there are no winners and no losers. Because each player acts the part of an imaginary character, they are an excellent way of escaping from the normal daily grind of life. There are dozens of different role-playing games and societies that run sessions. The first game developed was 'Dungeons and Dragons'. This is set, as its name suggests, in a fantastic medieval world. There are also games set in the present and in the future.

Usually played by children or teenagers, role-playing games stimulate the imagination and develop improvisation skills, and are an excellent way of developing self-confidence. Not everyone finds it easy to act in the correct manner in stressful or difficult situations, and for this reason exercises based on role-playing therapy are often used to demonstrate the appropriate responses to situations. Exercises based on this principle are sometimes used in therapy for stress, assertiveness training, and on company training courses.

In therapy for the treatment of stress, role-playing is used in the following manner: suppose a 'patient' is bullied by her boss and cannot strike back. The therapist will play the role of the boss and the patient will play herself, thus recreating the stressful situation in order to learn how to defuse it.

Similarly, on a company training course the participants may act out and improvise a situation they could encounter at work. In the case of sales staff, for example, they might practise getting out of an embarrassing situation or winning over a reluctant customer. In some stores, sales assistants are trained in pairs, one playing the assistant, the other the customer.

Role-playing offers the advantage of a wide choice of situations. During a session, the participants create an environment that may contain as many different situations as daily life. In role-playing with family or friends, the participant's professional life or medical problems need not come into play at all. Any setting can be chosen – the future, medieval Japan, the 1920s, and so on. All offer the same tools for reducing inhibitions and increasing self-confidence, and all demand improvisation in the face of unexpected circumstances. There is a basic manual available that tells you all you need to know about where the games are set and how they work.

GAMES PEOPLE PLAY

Medieval: *Dungeons and Dragons and Advanced Dungeons and Dragons – fantasy peopled by elves, trolls, fairies, dragons, etc.*

The 1920s: *The Call of Cthulhu – the Roaring Twenties and, behind the scenes, the author H. P. Lovecraft's own fantasy world.*

The present: *Vampire – night in the streets of Paris, London, Berlin, Boston, etc. Magna Veritas – angels infiltrate modern society.*

The future: *Bitumen – the world after the Apocalypse, in the universe of Mad Max. Shadowrun – In the age of virtual reality, cyberpirates take on the transnational corporations.*

Stress – information and help

BRITISH ASSOCIATION FOR COUNSELLING AND PSYCHOTHERAPY
1 Regent Place
Rugby
Warwickshire CV21 2PJ
Tel: 01788 550899
Fax: 01788 562189
E-mail: bac@bac.co.uk
Website:
www.counselling.co.uk
The Association maintains a list of counsellors in local areas.

COUNSELLING IN COMPANIES
23 Kensington Square
London W8 5HN
Tel: 020 7937 6224
Fax: 020 7376 1914
Website: ww.counselling
companies.co.uk
Helps organisations cope with the negative effects of stress on their employees at all levels.

INTERNATIONAL STRESS MANAGEMENT ASSOCIATION (ISMA)
PO Box 348
Waltham Cross EN8 8ZL
Tel: 07000 780430
E-mail:
stress@isma.org.uk
Website:
www.isma.org.uk
A registered charity with a multidisciplinary professional membership. ISMA exists to promote sound knowledge and best practice in the prevention and reduction of human stress. It sets professional standards for the benefit of individuals and organisations using the services of its members.

LONDON HEALTH
Website:
www.londonhealth.co.uk/
stressmanagement.asp
This site lists practitioners in stress management in the London area as well as details of courses, exercises and support groups.

MENTAL HEALTH IN THE UK
Website: www.mental-
health.freeserve.co.uk/
page2.html
This website is for people with any sort of mental health problems (depression, anxiety, Alzheimer's disease etc). There are links to advocacy teams, MIND, self-help groups and other useful sites.

NATIONAL ASSOCIATION FOR MANAGERS OF STUDENT SERVICES (UK) (NAMSS)
Website: www.namss.
org.uk/counsel.htm
NAMSS provides information and support for students and staff of colleges. This site has links to counselling, support and self-help groups and various mental health resources.

ROYAL COLLEGE OF PSYCHIATRISTS
Royal College of Psychiatrists Press and Public Information
Royal College of Psychiatrists
17 Belgrave Square,
London SW1X 8PG
Tel: 020 7235 2351
Fax: 020 7245 1231

THE SAMARITANS
10 The Grove
Slough
Berkshire SL1 1QP
Telephone helpline:
08457 90 90 90
or 1850 60 90 90 in the Republic of Ireland
Admin telephone:
01753 216500.
Fax: 01753 89004

E-mail: jo@samaritans.org
Website:
www.samaritans.org
The Samaritans is a registered charity based in the UK and Republic of Ireland that provides confidential emotional support to any person who is suicidal or despairing. The Samaritans service is available by phone, e-mail, writing, or by visiting one of their 203 local branches across the UK and Ireland.

STRESS UK
Website:
www.stress.org.uk/occs.
htm
Stress UK offers support and training in the management of occupational stress. The website has links to organisations offering programmes in this area.

HELP FOR PARENTS

ASSOCIATION FOR POST-NATAL ILLNESS (APNI)
25 Jerdan Place
London SW6 1BE
Tel: 020 7386 0868
A network of telephone and postal volunteers who have suffered from postnatal illness and offer information, support and encouragement on a one-to-one basis.

CRY-SIS (ENGLAND, WALES AND NORTHERN IRELAND)
BM Cry-Sis
London WC1N 3XX
Tel: 020 7404 5011
Offers help and support for parents whose children cry excessively, have a sleep problem or have temper tantrums and other behaviour difficulties.

PARENTLINE (ENGLAND AND NORTHERN IRELAND)
Endway House
The Endway
Hadleigh, Benfleet
Essex SS7 2AN
Tel: 01702 554782
Telephone helpline: 01702 559900
A voluntary self-help organisation offering confidential support to parents under stress. A network of local telephone helplines is operated by trained parents. Also offers information on local support groups.

PHOBIAS

FIRST STEPS TO FREEDOM
7 Avon Court, School Lane
Kenilworth
Warwickshire CV8 2GX
Email: info@firststeps.
demon.co.uk
Website:
www.firststeps.demon.co.
uk
Help for those who suffer from phobias, panic attacks, general anxiety, obsessive-compulsive disorders and tranquillizer withdrawal.

NATIONAL PHOBICS SOCIETY
Zion CHRC
Royce Road, Hulme
Manchester M15 5FQ
Tel: 0161 227 9898
Fax: 0161 227 9862
E-mail:
natphob.soc@good.co.uk
Website: www.phobics-
society.org.uk
A volunteer-led organisation helping those affected by anxiety disorders.

Tackling dependency

SMOKING

LIFESAVER (HEALTH EDUCATION AUTHORITY)
Website:
www.lifesaver.co.uk/lifesaver.html
The Lifesaver website offers support, advice and motivation to help you stop smoking.

ONLINE BOOKLET
15 Rue Erlanger, 75016
Paris
Website:
www.hebs.scot.nhs.uk/publics/smoke/smk1.htm
Advice from a counsellor who has been helping people stop smoking for 20 years.

NHS SMOKING HELPLINE
Tel: 0800 169 0169

ALCOHOL

ALCOHOLICS ANONYMOUS
Tel: 020 7352 3001
Website: www.alcoholics-anonymous.org.uk
Five telephone lines on this number. Callers are put in touch with their local AA group.

BBC KICK THE HABIT CAMPAIGN
Website:
www.bbc.co.uk/health/kth/index.shtml
This website explores alcohol, drug and other addictions and how to kick the habit.

DRUGS

ADFAM NATIONAL
Tel: 020 7928 8900
Website:
www.drugsinfo.org.uk
Provides a national telephone helpline for families and friends of drug users, offering confidential support and information and details of drug services nationwide.

DRUGS IN SCHOOLS HELPLINE
Tel: 0345 366 666
Telephone helpline for drug users, friends and families of drug users.

National Drugs Helpline (Health Education Authority)
Tel: 0800 77 66 00
The National Drugs Helpline is a 24-hour, seven days a week, UK-wide free and confidential telephone service offering advice and information for those who are concerned, or have questions, about drugs. The service is available to anyone, including drug users (current, recovering or past) their friends, family and colleagues.

PATIENT UK: DRUG AND SUBSTANCE ABUSE
Website:
www.patient.org.uk/illness/d/drug_abuse
This website offers information and support.

RELEASE
Daytime telephone:
020 7729 9904
24-hour telephone:
020 7603 8654
A drugs helpline.

Therapies and well-being

ACUPUNCTURE

BRITISH ACUPUNCTURE COUNCIL
Park House
206–208 Latimer Road
London W10 6RE
Tel: 020 8964 0222

THE BRITISH MEDICAL ACUPUNCTURE SOCIETY
Newton House
Newton Lane
Whitley
Warrington
Cheshire WA4 4JA
Tel 01925 730727
Fax: 01925 730492

ALEXANDER TECHNIQUE

THE SOCIETY OF TEACHERS OF ALEXANDER TECHNIQUE (STAT)
20 London House
266 Fulham Road
London SW10 9EL
Tel: 020 7351 0828

ALEXANDER TEACHING NETWORK
PO box 53
Kendal
Cumbria LA9 4UP

THE PROFESSIONAL ASSOCIATION OF ALEXANDER TEACHERS
Tel: 0121 4262108

AROMATHERAPY

AROMATHERAPY ORGANISATIONS COUNCIL
The AOC Secretary
PO Box 19834
London SE25 6WF
Tel: 020 8251 7912
Fax: 020 8251 7942
The UK governing body responsible for setting standards of practice. Their website contains links.

DUNROMIN AROMATHERAPY
Website:
www.dunromin.demon.co.uk/aromatherapy/aromatherapy.htm
This site has general articles about aromatherapy, an introduction to what aromatherapy is and how it fits with other therapies, and a history of aromatherapy and the use of essential oils. There are also lists of aromatherapists and professional organisations concerned with aromatherapy in the UK.

INSTITUTE OF TRADITIONAL HERBAL MEDICINE AND AROMATHERAPY (ITHMA)

34 California Road
Mistley, Essex
Tel: 01206 393465
Website:
www.aromatherapy-studies.com
ITHMA trains people in aromatherapy and therapeutic massage for membership of the Register of Qualified Aromatherapists.

THE INTERNATIONAL SOCIETY OF AROMATHERAPISTS

ISPA House
82 Ashby Road, Hinckley
Leics LE10 1SN
Tel: 01455 637987
Fax: 01455 890956

THE REGISTER OF QUALIFIED AROMATHERAPISTS

PO Box 3431
Danbury, Chelmsford
Essex CM3 4UA
Tel: 01245 227957
E-mail: admin@R-Q-A.
demon.co.uk

AURICULAR THERAPY

THE ASSOCIATION OF AURICULAR THERAPY

489 Lichfield Road
Four Oaks
Sutton Coldfield B74 4DL

AYURVEDIC MEDICINE

AYURVEDIC MEDICAL ASSOCIATION UK

59 Dulverton Road
Selsdon
South Croydon CR2 8JP
Tel: 020 8657 6147
Fax: 020 8333 7904
E-mail:
dr.moorthy@england.com
Website: www.natural-healing.co.uk/ayurvedi.htm

BACH FLOWER REMEDIES

DR EDWARD BACH FOUNDATION

Mount Vernon
Sotwell
Wallingford OX10 0PZ
Tel: 01491 834678

CHINESE MEDICINE

DR & HERBS

Broad Street Mall,
Reading, Berkshire
Tel: 0118 958 8488
Offers treatment to relieve stress, to overcome anger and depression, and to give up smoking. There are centres in various parts of England.

CHIROPRACTIC

THE BRITISH CHIROPRACTIC ASSOCIATION

Blagrave House
17 Blagrave Street
Reading
Berkshire RG1 1QB
Tel: 0118 950 5950

BRITISH ASSOCIATION FOR APPLIED CHIROPRACTIC

The Old Post Office
Cherry Street
Stratton Audley
Oxon OX6 9BA
Tel: 01869 277111

MCTIMONEY CHIROPRACTIC ASSOCIATION

21 High Street
Eynsham
Oxon OX8 1HE
Tel: 01865 880974

THE SCOTTISH CHIROPRACTIC ASSOCIATION

30 Raeburn Place
Edinburgh EH12 5NX

FLOWER ESSENCE THERAPY

THE FLOWER ESSENCE ASSOCIATION

Anubis House
Creswell Drive
Ravenstone
Leics LE6 2AG
Tel: 01491 834678

HERBAL MEDICINE

NATIONAL INSTITUTE OF MEDICAL HERBALISTS

56 Longbrook Street
Exeter EX4 6AH
Tel: 01392 426022

HOMEOPATHY

BRITISH HOMEOPATHIC ASSOCIATION

27a Devonshire Street
London W1N 1RJ
Tel: 020 7935 2163

HOMEOPATHY HOME

Website: www
.homeopathyhome.com
Links to services, suppliers, chat groups and information about homeopathy.

HOMEOPATHIC INFORMATION SERVICE

23 Berkeley Road
Bishopston
Bristol BS7 8HF
Tel: 0117 944 5147
Website:
www.hominf.org.uk

HOMEOPATHY MEDICAL ASSOCIATION

6 Livingstone Road
Gravesend
Kent DA12 5DZ
Tel: 01474 560336
E-mail: info@the-hme.org
Website:
www.homoeopathy.org
The Association has a register of qualified homeopaths, and the website offers information about pharmacies supplying homeopathic products, homeopathic clinics and therapy centres.

HOMEOPATHY ONLINE

Website:
www.lyghtforce.com/
HomeopathyOnline
An online journal about homeopathy.

THE SOCIETY OF HOMEOPATHS

2 Artizan Road
Northampton NN1 4HU
Tel: 01604 21400
Fax: 01604-22622

HYPNOTHERAPY

HYPNOSIS ON LINE IN THE UK

Website:
www.hypnosis.org.uk

THE NATIONAL REGISTER OF HYPNOTHERAPISTS AND PSYCHOTHERAPISTS

Suite B, 12 Cross Street
Nelson
Lancashire BB9 7EN
Tel 01282 716839

THE HYPNOTHERAPY SOCIETY

Administration
PO Box 15
Tenderden
Kent TN30 7ZE
Tel: 01580 765856

BHA HYPNOTHERAPY ASSOCIATION

Secretary: John Dove
Tel: 01257 792993

THE NATIONAL COUNCIL FOR HYPNOTHERAPY

PO Box 5779
Burton-on-the-Wolds
Loughborough LE12 5ZF
Tel: 01509 881477

MASSAGE

AYURVEDIC HEAD & SHOULDER MASSAGE

Savita Patel
151 Drummond Street
London NW1
Tel: 020 7388 9795 and
020 8348 6976
Based on principles originating in India, this type of massage drains the toxins from your body. You

will feel purified and extremely relaxed. There are various versions of this technique.

BODYHARMONICS CENTRE
Cheltenham
Website:
www.bodyharmonics.co.uk/welcome.htm
The centre offers therapy and Tui Na, Indonesian and Thai traditional massage and manipulation.

INTERNATIONAL REGISTER OF MASSAGE THERAPISTS
PO Box 553
Hatfield Peverel CM3 2QN
E-mail:
irmt eb@yahoo.co.uk
Website: www.irmt.co.uk

SHIATSU MASSAGE
The Shiatsu Society of Great Britain
31 Pullman Lane
Godalming
Surrey GU7 1XY
Tel: 01483 860771
In Shiatsu massage, the masseur's fingers run along the meridians of the body, to harmonise the vital energy flows in the body. An ideal complement to acupuncture, this form of massage can relieve many ailments.

THE BRITISH SCHOOL OF SHIATSU-DO
East-West Centre
188 Old Street
London EC1V 9BP

PSYCHOTHERAPY

UK COUNCIL FOR PSYCHOTHERAPY (UKCP)
167–169 Great Portland St
London W1N 5FB
Tel: 020 7436 3002
Fax: 020 7436 3013
E-mail: ukcp@psychotherapy.org.uk
Website:www.psychotherapy.org.uk
UKCP is the largest national umbrella organisation for psychotherapy and

maintains a voluntary register of about 5000 qualified psychotherapists

REFLEXOLOGY

THE ASSOCIATION OF REFLEXOLOGISTS
27 Old Gloucester Street
London WC1N 3XX
Tel: 01892 512612
Website: www.aor.org.uk

INTERNATIONAL FEDERATION OF REFLEXOLOGISTS
76–78 Edridge Road
Croydon
Surrey CR0 1EF
Tel: 020 8667 9458

RECORDINGS

ARC MUSIC
PO Box 111
East Grinstead
West Sussex RH19 4FZ
Tel: 01342 328567
Fax: 01342 315958
E-mail:
info@arcmusic.co.uk
Website:
www.arcmusic.co.uk
CDs of world and folk music.

CYGNUS BOOKS
PO Box 15
Llandeilo SA19 6YX
Tel: 01550 777701
Fax: 01550 777569
E-mail: info@cygnus-books.co.uk
Website: www.cygnus-books.co.uk
Publishes a CD of uninterrupted bird song recorded in the wild in Ireland.

NEW WORLD MUSIC
Paradise Farm
Weatherall, Halesworth
Suffolk IP19 8RH

ROYAL SOCIETY FOR THE PROTECTION OF BIRDS
The Lodge
Sandy, Bedfordshire
Publishes recordings of British bird song.

Further Reading

Life and how to survive it, by Robin Skynner and John Cleese. Vermilion, 1997

Depression at work, by Vicky Maud. Sheldon Press, 2000

Overcoming depression. A self-help guide using cognitive behavioral techniques, by Paul Gilbert. Robinson, 2000

Person-centred therapy today, by Dave Mearns and Brian Thorne. Sage, 2000

Towards emotional literacy, by Susie Orbach. Virago, 1999

Aromatherapy

Aromatherapy: An A – Z, by Patricia Davis. Daniel, 1988

Aromatherapy workbook, by Shirley Price. Thorsons, 1993

Practical Aromatherapy, by Shirley Price. Thorsons, 1987

Aromatherapy for everyone, by Robert Tisserand. Penguin, 1988

The encyclopaedia of essential oils, by Julia Lawless. Element, 1992

Ayurvedic medicine

The handbook of Ayurveda, by Dr Shantha Godagama. Cygnus Books. Website: www.cygnus-books.co.uk

Hypnosis

Self-hypnosis. A self-help guide, by Valerie Austin. Thorsons, 1992.

Phobias

Fight your phobia and win, by David Lewis. Sheldon Press, 1990

For people who panic, by Martin Landau-North. Anthos Park Publishers, 1985

Self-help for your nerves, by Claire Weekes. Fontana, 1991

Fears and phobias, by Isaac Marks. Heinneman, 1969

Well-being

The Body Shop book of wellbeing, Ebury Press, 1998.

The feeling good handbook, by David D. Burns. Plume, 1999

Glossary

ACETYLCHOLINE

A chemical messenger secreted by neurones (nerve cells) that that has a huge variety of effects and is involved in almost every response of the body in one way or another. Nicotine mimics its effect.

ADRENAL GLANDS

Glands located above the kidneys, consisting of an internal part (medulla) and an external one (cortex). They produce stress hormones (glucocorticoids and adrenaline).

ADRENALINE

A chemical messenger secreted by neurones (nerve cells) and the adrenal glands. It helps to stimulate the systems of the body, especially the blood vessels.

ADRENAL CORTEX

The outer part of the adrenal glands, located above the kidneys. Produces the steroid hormones, eg the glucocorticoids.

ALLERGEN

A substance that sets off an allergic reaction.

ANXIETY

Prolonged experience of fear, stress or emotional tension.

AURICULAR THERAPY

A form of acupuncture in which acupuncture points on the external ear are stimulated to treat pain, dyslexia and other functional imbalances.

AUTOIMMUNE ILLNESSES

Disorders in which the immune system attacks the body itself, such as rheumatoid arthritis and thyroid disease.

BIOFEEDBACK

A technique for assessing stress and learning to relax.

CEREBRAL CORTEX

The outer part of the brain.

COGNITIVE THERAPY

A form of psychotherapy used in the treatment of a variety of problems, including depression, anxiety, obsessions and phobias. Cognitive therapists help people to identify and change the thought processes that lead to these problems.

CORTISOL

This steroid hormone, produced by the adrenal glands, is important in the control of blood sugar levels and the stress reaction. Also called hydrocortisone.

CYCLOTHYMIC

Describes a milder form of being manic-depressive. A person who alternates periods of hyperactivity with bouts of depression.

DEPRESSION

A psychological disorder whose symptoms are sadness and low mood, slowing down of physical and mental processes, and loss of enjoyment and energy. When people talk about being depressed they do not always mean they have a medical condition; often it is simply a question of anxiety, distress or sadness.

ENDORPHIN

A chemical messenger present in the hypo-thalamus and pituitary gland that has pain-killing properties. Morphine mimics its effect.

ERGONOMICS

The study of how people's performance at work is influenced by their environment, the equipment and systems they use, and their own anatomy, physiology and psychology.

FREE RADICALS

Unstable chemicals that cause oxidation in cells, damaging mainly the larger molecules, such as DNA. They are thought to be involved in ageing.

GENERAL ADAPTATION SYNDROME

A predesigned series of bodily reactions triggered in response to many different types of stress. These processes, occurring in the cardiovascular system, respiratory system and brain, are set off by nervous impulses and hormonal secretions triggered by a stressor. This phenomenon was described by Hans Selye in 1936 and matches the current definition of stress, although it does not take account of variation among individuals.

GLUCOCORTICOIDS

Hormones produced by the cortex of the adrenal glands, such as cortisol.

HIPPOCAMPUS

An area of the brain involved in formulating and storing memories.

HYPOTHALAMUS AND PITUITARY GLAND

The hypothalamus is situated at the base of the brain. By sending messages through the nervous system and via chemical messengers called neurotransmitters and by controlling the secretion of hormones into the blood by the pituitary gland, it controls the body's vital functions (hunger, thirst, sexual activity, sleep and waking, temperature regulation).

LIMBIC SYSTEM

The part of the brain that manages the emotions, motivation and certain types of memory.

MALIGNANT GROWTH

A cancerous tumour, as distinct from a benign tumour. Malignant tumours spread beyond their original site of growth into surrounding areas and other parts of the body.

NEUROENDOCRINE SYSTEM

This system consists of specially adapted nerve cells that release chemical messengers that act as hormones, and nerve cells that control the release of hormones from glands such as the adrenal medulla.

NEUROTRANSMITTERS

Chemical messengers that transmit information between neurones in the brain and nerves.

PSYCHOACTIVE DRUGS

Drugs that affect the mind or behaviour, such as anxiolytics, antidepressants and sleeping tablets.

PSYCHOSOMATIC

Describes physical or functional disorders caused or worsened by psychological factors. The word comes from 'psyche' (all psychological processes collectively) and 'soma' (things that are purely of the body).

SEROTONIN

This chemical messenger is extremely important in the brain, being involved in pain suppression, maintaining high moods and possibly sleep. Some antidepressant drugs work by maintaining it at high levels in the brain.

SOMATIC CONVERSION

A process in which a stressor such as emotional conflict has a physical effect on the body in some way, either on a certain organ or tissue or affecting a physiological process, such as digestion or sleep.

SYMPATHETIC AND PARASYMPATHETIC NERVOUS SYSTEMS

These form the autonomic nervous system, which controls involuntary processes in the body. They work against each other in such a way that they are able to regulate the internal organs and glands to a minutely precise degree.

THYMUS GLAND

A gland behind the sternum that functions in childhood and whose action diminishes during adolescence. It plays an important role in building the adult immune system.

ULCER

A sore caused by breakdown of the skin or a mucous membrane, for instance inside the mouth and the stomach lining.

Contents

Fact ⊗ 2–10
Fun facts and quick quotes

Discover ⊗ 11–44

Look ⟫ 45–68
Images to please the eye and calm the spirit

In practice ⟫ 69–98

Find out ⟫ 99–125

Credits

P. 4, Cosmos/SPL/P. Brown – P. 12, Rock carvings, Akakus, Libya. Photograph: Explorer/R. Mattes. – P. 15, *The four states of society: poverty*, Miniature by Jean Bourdichon, Beaux-Arts library, Paris. Photograph: Hachette photographic library. – P. 16, Statuette by Oscar Nemon. Freud Museum, London. Photograph: The Bridgeman Art Library. – P. 19, The Image Bank/Archive Photos. – P. 21, Cosmos/SPL/M. Kulyk. – P. 22, Cosmos / S.P.L. / A. Hart-Davis – P. 25, Cosmos/Popperfoto. – P. 26, Philippe Ughetto – P. 28, Urba Images / J.-C. Pattacini – P. 31, Silk-screen print, Paris, 1998, Ernest Pignin-Ernest. © Adagp 2000. – P. 32, Tomography of two brains. Photograph: Cosmos/SPL/Wellcome. – P. 35, Grozny, Chechnya, 1996. Photograph: Magnum/J. Natchwey. – P. 36, Cosmos/SPL/M. Kulyk. – P. 39, Cosmos / S.P.L. / A. Pasieka – P. 41, *Symbolic head*, R. B. D. Wells. Photograph: Explorer/Mary Evans. – P. 42, Charlie Chaplin in *Modern Times*, Charlie Chaplin (1936) ; Photograph: Hachette photographic library. – P. 46-47, Photogram, Stone/A. Roberts. – P. 48-49, Fotogram-Stone/J. Jangoux. – P. 50-51, Fotogram-Stone/J. Walker P. 53-53,. Rapho/J. E. Pasquier. P. 54-55, Rapho/Yamashita. P. 56-57, Fotogram-Stone/Ryan-Beyer. P. 58-59, Fotogram-Stone/S. Nourse – P. 60-61, Fotogram-Stone/G. Allison. – P. 62-63, Fotogram-Stone/H. Strand. – P. 64-65, Fotogram-Stone/J. Rajs. – P. 66-67, Fotogram-Stone/G. Gulin. – P. 68, Fotogram–Stone/V. Pearson.

Acknowledgements

The authors wish to thank Dr Mathias Russik for his authority and insight.